People Need People

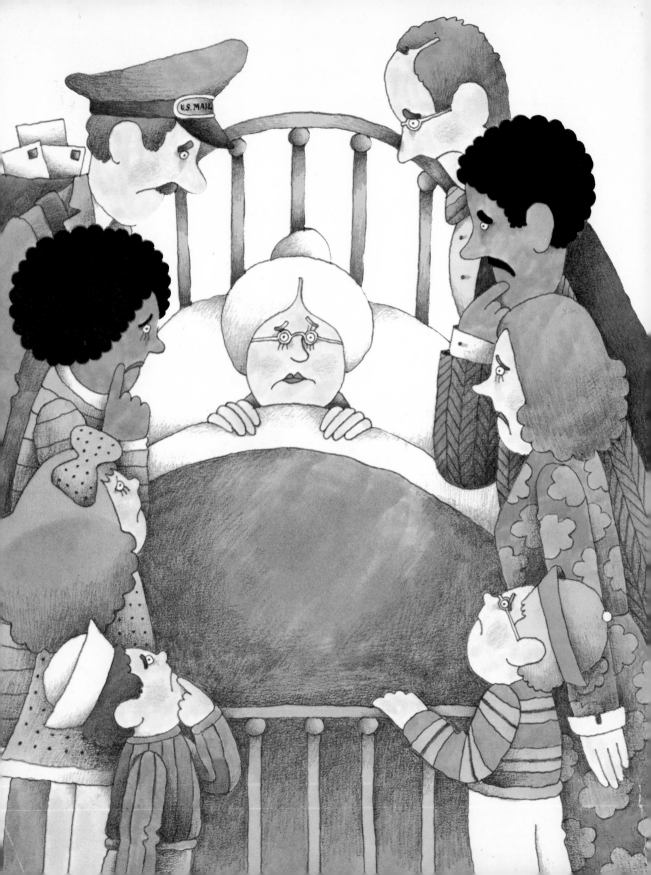

People Need People

Eldonna L. Evertts / Language Arts
Lyman C. Hunt / Reading
Bernard J. Weiss / Linguistics and Curriculum

Edited by Jane Berkowitz and Craig Bettinger
Educational Consultants: Patsy Montague and Janet Sprout

THE HOLT BASIC READING SYSTEM
• LEVEL 9 •

HOLT, RINEHART AND WINSTON, INC.
New York / Toronto / London / Sydney

Illustrated by

Blair Drawson, pages 12-20
Tad Krumeich, pages 21, 67, 131, 215, 223
Bob Pepper, pages 22-29
Ingbet, photos: pages 30-31, 53-66, 252
Miriam Schottland, pages 32-43
Bernice Myers, pages 44-52
Lionel Kalish, pages 70-79
Viewpoint Graphics, pages 80, 187
Lorraine Fox, pages 81-91
Ray Cruz, pages 92-101
Bill Powers, page 102
Marie Michal, pages 103, 214
Bernie D'Andrea, pages 104-111, 243-251
Jerome Snyder, pages 112-129
Loretta Lustig, pages 130, 205, 245-246, 248-250
Diane de Groat, pages 134-143, 224-239
Norman Green, pages 144-145
Bob Owens, pages 146-166
Tim and Greg Hildebrandt, pages 167-186
Jack Endewelt, pages 188-204
Muriel Wood, pages 208-213
Edward Towles, pages 240-241
Cover, pages 10-11, 68-69, 132-133, and 206-207
   constructed by S. N. Studio.

Acknowledgments

Grateful acknowledgment is made to the following authors and publishers:

The Dial Press, for "Marvin's Manhole," adapted from *Marvin's Manhole* by Winifred Rosen. Copyright © 1970 by Winifred Rosen. Used by permission.

Contents

Thinking of Others

Four Scary Things

How Would You Feel?

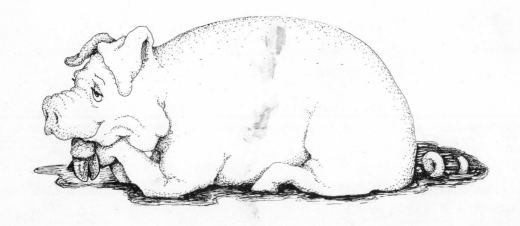

What Would You Do?

Alice James Napjus

Freddy Found a Frog

Freddy made a small boat and put it
in some water to see if it would go.
He put a small stone in the boat for one man
and a big stone for another man.
But when he put in a very big stone,
it was too much for the little boat.

The boat went down in the water.

Freddy put his hand way down in the water
to get the boat. He found something, but it wasn't
his boat. It was a frog. A big green frog!

"What a beautiful frog!" said Freddy.

The frog may have heard Freddy because it said,

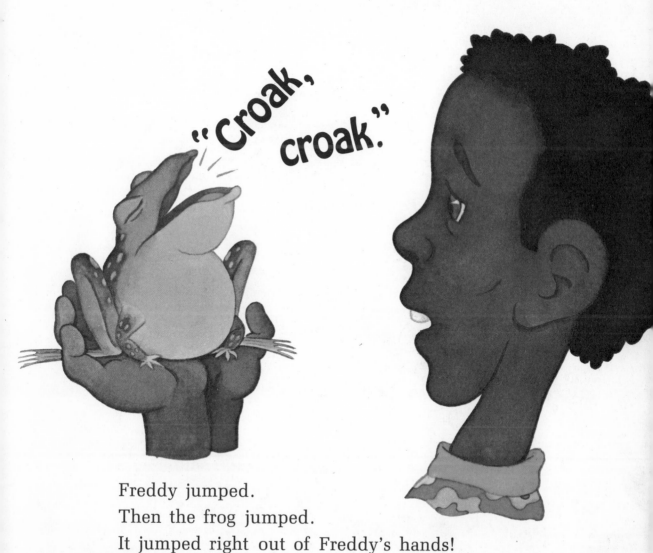

"Croak, croak."

Freddy jumped.

Then the frog jumped.

It jumped right out of Freddy's hands!

"Frog, where are you?" asked Freddy.

There it was, right near Freddy's hand.
Freddy wasn't going to let the frog get away
this time. He picked it up.

"This isn't a good place for you," said Freddy.
"I'm going to find a home for you."

He put the frog into his pocket and walked
up the street.

As Freddy walked, he began to sing.
Now and then the frog would help him out
by saying,

Freddy stopped when he saw Mr. Mays.
But Freddy didn't take his hand from his pocket.
"Good morning," said Freddy. Then he asked,
"Mr. Mays, what would you do with a frog?"

"I don't have a frog," said Mr. Mays.
"But if I did, I would take it fishing."

Freddy laughed. "Frogs can't fish," he said.

"No, no," said Mr. Mays. "The frog would be
my bait. It would help me get the fish."

The frog gave a jump in Freddy's pocket.

"Bait!" said Freddy. "No, no. Not my frog!"
He ran down the street. He wasn't going
to let his frog be anyone's bait.

Mr. Mays looked at Freddy as he ran off.
"Now what did I say to make him do that?"
he thought.

The Best Place

Freddy saw Miss Penny walking down the street.

"Hello, Freddy," said Miss Penny.

"Hello, Miss Penny," said Freddy. "May I ask you something? If you had a frog, what would you do with it?"

"If I had a frog," said Miss Penny, "I know just what I'd do. I'd cook it. Frog legs are very good to eat."

When Freddy heard that, he began to run
again. He wanted to get home. The frog gave
a little jump in Freddy's pocket.

"It's all right, little frog," said Freddy.
"I'll take you home. I'll find a good place
for you there."

Freddy found his mother picking flowers
in back of their house. Freddy looked
at his mother for a long time
without saying anything.

At last he said, "Mother, what would you do
if you had a frog?"

"If I had a frog, I'd put him in my little pond.
That's the best place for a frog, Freddy," said Mother.

Freddy put his hand in his pocket,
and the frog gave another little jump.
"It's all right, frog," he said. "I found
a good home for you."

Freddy ran to the pond and let the frog jump
out of his hand and into the pond.
Then Freddy saw him jump up onto
a big white flower in the middle of the pond.
He looked very green, sitting there
on the white flower.

Just then Freddy's mother came over to the pond.

"Look, Mother," said Freddy. "My frog likes
his new home. Isn't he beautiful?"

"Yes, Freddy," Mother said. "He is."

And Freddy's frog said,

"Croak."

Where Do Words Come From?

Words come from many places. Our word *frog* comes from a very old word *pravate*. It means *he jumps up.* Do you think that fits the meaning of *frog*?

The word *flower* comes from *flor.* It is an old word that meant *the best of anything.* Is that a good meaning for *flower*?

Word Derivations. Have each paragraph read. Discuss the derivations of the two words.

LUCY
and her
COUSIN

Elizabeth Levy

Lucy's cousin Amy wasn't anything
like Lucy. She wasn't as big, and she
wasn't as old. Amy was very good
and very clean. Not at all
like Lucy!

If Amy was coming to Lucy's house,
Lucy's mother would say, "Lucy,
try to be as clean as Amy today.
Amy is not as big as you are,
and she is not as old, but she is
a very good little girl."

Lucy didn't care too much for the days that Amy came to play. Lucy liked to play with her friend Herman. Best of all, she and Herman liked to paint. Lucy would get paint on Herman, and Herman would get paint on Lucy.

Lucy liked to play with her friend Goldie, too. They would go to the park and play in the mud. They would make mud monsters and throw mud at them.

But Lucy didn't have much fun with Amy. Amy liked to play house. Amy would be the mother and put on Lucy's mother's clothes. She would look a long time in the mirror and say,

"M-m-m, my! I'm getting too fat."

Amy made Lucy play the father and tell her that she was not fat at all.

As games go, it was not too much fun for Lucy.

One day Lucy's mother said, "Amy is coming
for the night. Your aunt has to go on a trip,
and your cousin Amy can't be all alone. Now
you have to be good and do what Amy wants.
After all, she is not as big as you,
and she is not as old."

So Amy came over in the afternoon. They played
ladies going to the store. Then they played ladies
in the elevators and had fun with all the buttons.
But Amy's games were not as much fun
as mud monsters.

That night when the girls were alone in Lucy's room,
Lucy said,

"When my mother tells me I have
to go to sleep, lots of times
I don't go to sleep at all.
I take my radio into bed, and I
play it so quietly that no one
knows. When we go to bed,
I'll let you play it, too!"

But Amy said,

"You can't do that. I have to go
to sleep. My mother told me to be a good girl,
and she says I have to get my sleep. I'm going
to tell your mother if you play your radio."

"Oh, be quiet. You're just
a little girl, and you're not as much fun
as my other friends,"

Just then, Lucy's daddy came in, put out the lights,
and said,

GOOD NIGHT.

Lucy was just about asleep when she heard someone crying. It was Amy, sitting up in bed and crying.

"Why are you crying?"

"I want my mother. I don't like it here. I want to go home."

"Stop crying. And don't get my daddy up."

But Amy couldn't stop crying. And Lucy didn't know what to do.

Then Lucy said,

"Come over to my bed."

Amy did. They got under the covers,
and Amy stopped crying a little.

Lucy got her radio and put it on
under the covers. Lucy began to sing
with the radio. Then Amy stopped her crying
and began singing, too.

So under the covers, where no one heard,
Amy and Lucy and the radio were all singing.

By now, Amy and Lucy didn't want to sleep at all.
They were having too much fun. They laughed
and played the radio long into the night.

After that night, Amy and Lucy didn't become best friends. Amy still liked playing house best, and Lucy still liked playing in the mud.

Amy was still very clean
and very good. She wasn't as big,
and she wasn't as old.

But she wasn't all that bad.

Night Whispers

Sh-h-h, we must whisper.
The lights are out, so
we should be sleeping.
But I still have so
many things to say
that I can't sleep yet.

It's so nice you're here.
Remember last time
you stayed at my house?
It was Saturday.
You were so silly
when we snuck downstairs.

Tomorrow I have
something to show you.
It's a new secret
spot I know you'll like.
It's someplace I'm sure
no one's ever seen.

We'll go at sunrise.
Don't you think that's best?
That way no one will
see us and follow.

Why don't you say something?
Are you sleeping?

—Marci Ridlon

Peggy Parish

A SPECIAL NAME

Little Indian sat on a log with Big Hunter.
"Why don't I have a special name, Father?"
asked Little Indian. "I want a name just for me."

"An Indian has to find his own name,"
said Big Hunter. "I got my name because I was
a good hunter of big animals."

"Now I see," said Little Indian. "I'll go
and find a name, too."

Little Indian went into the forest. He walked very quietly. A good hunter makes no noise when he walks in the forest.

Little Indian heard something that made him stop. Tweet, tweet, tweet. Little Indian was quiet. Again he heard, tweet, tweet, tweet. Then he saw what was making the noise.

"Birds," said Little Indian. "What bright feathers they have! If I can pick some of their feathers, then I could be called Bright Feather."

Little Indian ran to the birds. But he couldn't get any of them. Every time he reached out to get them, they would fly to another place.

"If you won't let me pick some of your feathers," said Little Indian, "then I can't have the name Bright Feather."

Little Indian tried again and again to get some feathers, but at last he gave up.

"Bright Feather would have been a good name, but I'll just have to find another one," said Little Indian.

Little Indian walked far into the forest. He saw
a little brown rabbit eating, and he stopped.

"*H-m-m*," he said. "A rabbit's foot is lucky.
If I had a rabbit's foot, I could be called
Lucky Rabbit. I've got to get that rabbit."

The rabbit tried to run away,
but he couldn't get away from Little Indian.
Little Indian picked up the rabbit and said,
"Now I'll have my own special name."

But the rabbit didn't care about a special name
for Little Indian. He just wanted to get away.

"It's all right," Little Indian told the rabbit.
"I only want one foot. You will still have three."

But the rabbit looked at Little Indian
with his big eyes.

"I just can't do it," said Little Indian.
He put the rabbit down, and the rabbit ran away.
"Maybe I'll find another name," he said.

Snapping Turtle

As Little Indian sat down on a log,
he heard a noise. "Something is coming," he said.

Just then a porcupine came walking by.
Little Indian laughed. "Oh," he said.
"It's only a porcupine."

Little Indian was going to walk away,
but he stopped.

"Quills!" he said. "Porcupines have quills.
My mother puts quills on our clothes. I'll pick
a few for her. That's it! Quill Picker!
That's the name I want."

"Porcupine," said Little Indian. "I want
to be called Quill Picker. So I'm going
to pick a few of the quills from your tail.
That's where the best ones are."

Little Indian walked around the porcupine.
But the porcupine walked around Little Indian, too.

"Stop that!" said Little Indian. "You have
lots of quills. I only want a few. Don't you want
my name to be Quill Picker?"

But every time Little Indian tried to run
around the porcupine, the porcupine ran
around him. Little Indian couldn't reach
the porcupine's tail.

Little Indian jumped up and down.
"If that's the way you want it," he said,
"I don't care about your old quills!"

The porcupine ran away, and Little Indian
walked down to the river. He wasn't very happy.
He didn't know what to do about finding
his own special name. "I'm just not lucky,"
he said.

As Little Indian was looking at the river,
he saw a small head bobbing up and down
in the water.

"Why, it's a turtle!" said Little Indian. He saw
the turtle swim over to a log and climb up on it.

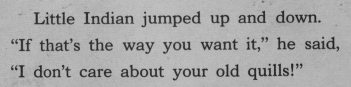

"H-m-m," said Little Indian. "Turtle soup!
Maybe I'll be lucky and get that turtle."

Little Indian got into the water and began
to swim over to the log. When he got there,
he reached for the turtle. But the turtle climbed down
off the log and went back into the river.

Little Indian saw the turtle go under the water
and swim away. "No, you don't," said Little Indian.
He went under the water and began to swim
after the turtle.

"I won't let you get away," said Little Indian.

This time he went way down under the water
to look for the turtle. When he came back up,
he had mud all over him, but no turtle!

"That was my last try," he said. "I just can't get a special name. I'm not very lucky."

Little Indian wasn't happy as he walked home.

When Little Indian got home, he found Big Hunter waiting for him.

"Your pants are covered with mud," said Big Hunter. "What have you been doing?"

"I was trying to get a turtle in the river," said Little Indian. "But I wasn't very lucky."

"Go into the house and put on some clean pants," said Big Hunter.

As Little Indian walked away, Big Hunter began to laugh. "So," he said, "you got a turtle name."

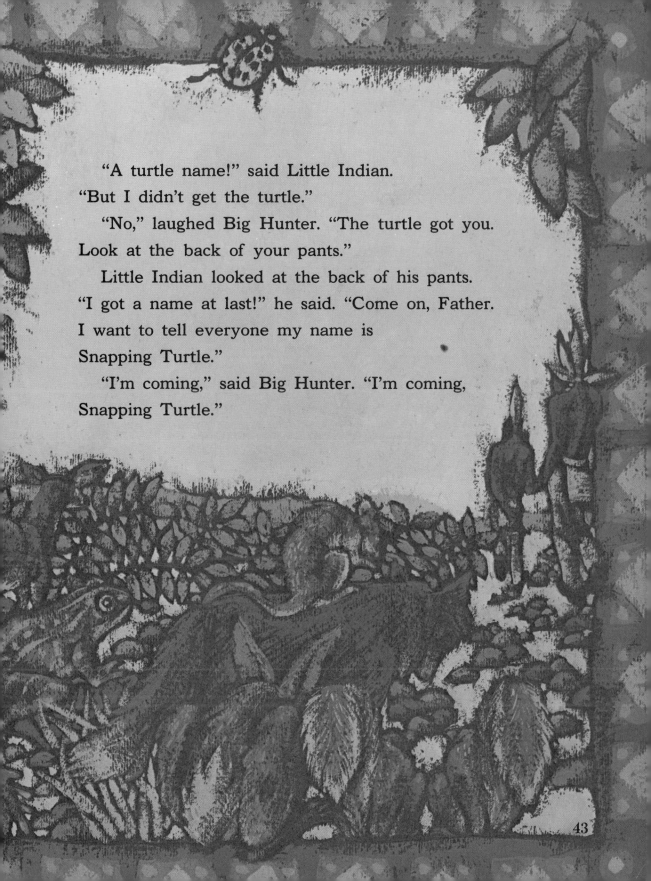

"A turtle name!" said Little Indian.
"But I didn't get the turtle."

"No," laughed Big Hunter. "The turtle got you.
Look at the back of your pants."

Little Indian looked at the back of his pants.
"I got a name at last!" he said. "Come on, Father.
I want to tell everyone my name is
Snapping Turtle."

"I'm coming," said Big Hunter. "I'm coming,
Snapping Turtle."

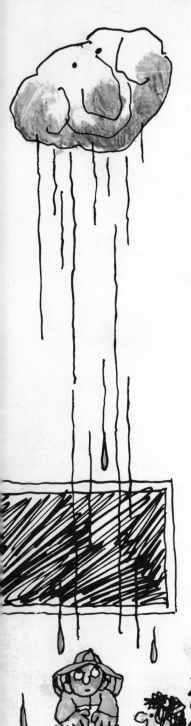

Michael and Joanne Cole

Wet Albert

Clouds come, and clouds go.
But there was one cloud that came
and didn't go. It came
floating along in the sky one day
and stopped over a little boy
called Albert. And it rained.

The cloud went everywhere with Albert.
And everywhere they went, it rained.
When Albert went to the park
with his sister, the two of them had
to play in the rain.

When Albert went for a walk
with his mother, she got wet, too.
And when Albert went to school, he got
the room all wet. Albert was asked
to do his schoolwork at home.

44

When Wet Albert was home, so much rain
came down on his house that in no time at all
there was water all over the house. Wet Albert
and his mother and father and sister had
to climb on top of the house.
When the water got to the top of the house,
they all had to jump onto a bed that came
floating out of Albert's room. The bed went
floating along with Albert and his family.
In time they came to a river.

"Let's live on the river!" said Wet Albert.

"On a bed, Albert?" asked his mother.

"No, on a boat!" said his father. "Good idea!
A little rain on the river will be all right."

So Wet Albert's family set up house on an old boat.
Wet Albert's father got him a little boat of his own.
Whenever anyone wanted to sit in the sun,
Albert would go off alone on his boat and fish.

Albert's father had to have work,
so he thought about what he could do
on the river. Then he got an idea.
He could take things from place to place
along the river—pigs, cows, clothes, flowers, books.
Everything and anything! He could bring people
whatever they wanted. And that is what he did.

"This is the life," said Wet Albert's father.
"This is the life."

And the days went by like the trees along the river.

The Drought

That summer there was a drought in the town
where Wet Albert had lived. Day after day
went by with no rain. The sun had dried up all the rivers.
All but Wet Albert's! It was
the only river that had water.
Wet Albert and his family were
still floating up and down the river
in their boat.

Life was good for Wet Albert and his family.
But not for the people in the little town!
Because of the drought, not a thing would grow.
How could anything grow without rain?

There was very little for the people and animals
to eat. And there wouldn't be anything to eat
all that winter if there was no rain
to help things grow.

It was lucky that there was one cloud in the sky that summer. And that cloud was Wet Albert's!

"Let's get Wet Albert to help us," said the farmers. "If he comes to our farms, he will bring rain."

Wet Albert was happy to help the farmers. He went to all the farms, and wherever he went, the rain from his cloud made the farms green. Things began to grow again.

Then Albert went to all the rivers, and his rain cloud put water back into them.

Thanks to Wet Albert there was a harvest that fall,
and a good harvest, too. When all the harvest
was in, the farmers took some of it to Wet Albert
and his family.

People around the world heard the news
of Wet Albert. Wherever there was a drought,
people would say, "Get Wet Albert!"

But how could he get to places all around the world?

One man had a good idea. "Get the boy
a helicopter," he said. "Then he can
bring rain to everyone!"

So Wet Albert got a helicopter of his own.
He went all over the world bringing rain
wherever there was a drought.

But after every trip, he was happy to come back to his family on the old boat.

"Nothing like a drop of rain to make the place look like home again," said Albert's father.

After that, Albert had the helicopter right there on the boat with him. Then he could take off right away if there was another drought.

Clouds come, and clouds go.
But if you ever see a cloud come and go with a helicopter under it, you'll know that there is a drought somewhere. And Wet Albert is on his way with rain.

April Rain Song

Let the rain kiss you.
Let the rain beat upon your head
   with silver liquid drops.
Let the rain sing you a lullaby.
The rain makes still pools
   on the sidewalk.
The rain makes running pools
   in the gutter.
The rain plays a little sleep-song
   on our roof at night—
And I love the rain.

—Langston Hughes

The Brothers Grimm

Rumpelstiltskin

PART ONE

An old man had a very beautiful daughter.
One day the old man went to see the king.
He wanted to let the king know that he was
someone special. When the king came into the room,
the old man said, "I have a daughter who can
spin gold out of straw."

"You have?" said the king. "If your daughter can
spin gold out of straw, I'd like to see her.
Bring her to me in the morning, and I will see
what she can do."

So the next day the old man came to the castle
with his daughter. The king took the girl
to a small room that had lots of straw.
Then the king said, "Now get to work. I want you
to spin this straw into gold tonight.
I'll come back in the morning to get the gold."

The girl sat alone in the room. She didn't know
how to spin straw into gold, and she began to cry.

Just then the door opened, and a funny-looking
little man came in. "Hello," he said.
"Why are you crying?"

"The king wants me to spin gold out of this straw by tonight, and I don't know how to do it," said the girl.

The little man asked, "What will you give me if I spin it for you?"

"I'll give you this little gold mirror," said the girl.

The little man took the mirror, sat down, and began to spin the straw. He worked all night, and by morning he had made gold out of all the straw.

When the king came into the room in the morning, he was very happy to see all the gold. He took the old man's daughter to another room that had lots of straw. The king told the girl to spin the straw into gold that night.

When the girl saw all that straw, she began to cry again. She still didn't know how to spin straw into gold.

The door opened, and the same little man came in. "What will you give me this time if I spin the straw into gold for you?" he asked the girl.

"I'll give you my ring," she said.

The little man took the ring and sat down and began to spin the straw. By morning he had made gold out of all the straw.

The king came into the room the next morning and was very happy to see all the gold. He took the girl to a very big room that had lots of straw. The king told her to spin all the straw into gold. "If you can spin all this straw into gold by morning, you will be my queen," he said.

When the girl was alone, the little man came into the room again. And again he asked, "What will you give me if I spin the straw for you?"

"I don't have anything to give you," said the girl.

"If you become queen and have a child, give me the child," said the little man.

The girl saw no other way to get help. So she said she would give the little man what he asked. The man sat down to spin. He worked all night, and by morning he had made gold out of all the straw.

part two

When the king came into the room in the morning,
he found all the gold he could ever want.
"You will be my queen," he said to the girl.
"And you will not have to spin straw ever again."
So the next day the old man's daughter became a queen.

Some time after that, the king and queen had
a beautiful child. The queen was so happy, she forgot
all about the funny-looking little man. But one day
the door to her room opened, and there he was.

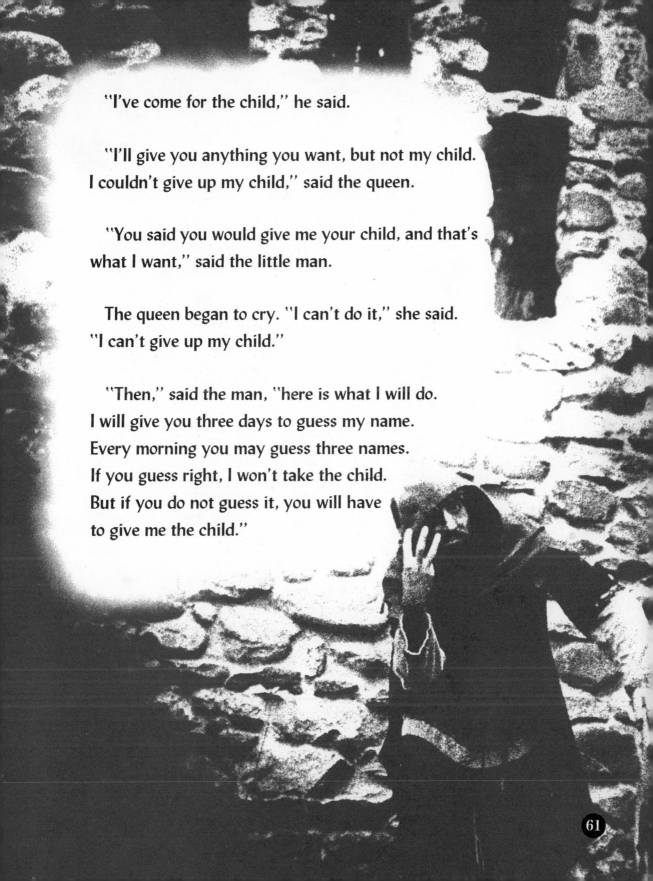

"I've come for the child," he said.

"I'll give you anything you want, but not my child.
I couldn't give up my child," said the queen.

"You said you would give me your child, and that's
what I want," said the little man.

The queen began to cry. "I can't do it," she said.
"I can't give up my child."

"Then," said the man, "here is what I will do.
I will give you three days to guess my name.
Every morning you may guess three names.
If you guess right, I won't take the child.
But if you do not guess it, you will have
to give me the child."

That night the queen thought of every name
she had ever heard. Then she called her page
and told him to go out and find other names.

In the morning when the little man came to the castle,
the queen tried to guess his name.

"Is your name Mr. Appleflower?" she asked.

"No," said the little man.

"Is it Mr. Greenpot?" asked the queen.

"No," said the man.

"Is it Mr. Crabtree?" she asked.

"No," said the little man. "You didn't guess it.
I'll be back in the morning, and you can try again."

The next day the queen asked for names from people who lived near the castle. When the little man came to the castle, the queen tried to guess his name again.

"Is your name Mr. Birdwing?" she asked.

"No," said the little man.

"Is it Mr. Whitecoat?" she asked.

"No," he said.

"Is it Mr. Tigerbutton?" she asked.

"No," he said. "You can try again in the morning." And with that the man was gone.

On the last day the page ran to the queen. "I found
a new name," he said. "In a house in the forest,
a funny-looking little man was singing.
He was singing about a queen's child and how lucky
he was that no one would know his name was
Rumpelstiltskin."

The queen was very happy when she heard the name
Rumpelstiltskin. She thanked the page and went
to her room to wait for the little man.

When the little man came to the castle, he said, "Can you guess my name today?"

"Is your name Mr. Goodfish?" the queen asked.

"No," said the man.

"Is it Mr. Pennypond?" she asked.

"No," he said.

"Could it be Rumpelstiltskin?" asked the queen.

The little man began jumping up and down. "How did you guess?" he cried.

But the queen wouldn't tell him. She called her page and told him to take the man away.

And that was the last anyone ever saw of the funny-looking little man.

GIANT WORDS

What's the longest word you know?

Porcupine

Schoolhouse

Helicopter

Thanksgiving

Tyrannosaurus

Rumpelstiltskin

Do you know a word longer than Rumpelstiltskin?

Word Configuration. Have the words read and their length discussed. Let the children think of other long words.

Thinking of Others

Mildred Kantrowitz

maxie

Maxie lived alone in three small rooms
in an old brownstone house on Cherry Street.
She had lived there a long time,
and every day was the same for Maxie.

Every morning at 7:00, up went the shades
on Maxie's living room windows.
Every morning at 7:10, Maxie's cat ran
over to the middle window.
He sat down to look at the people
on the street.

At 7:20, if you were looking
at Maxie's back window, you could see
the shade go up. At 7:22, Maxie gave
her bird some water and something to eat.
When the bird began to sing,
everyone knew it was 7:22.

At 8:15 every morning, Maxie's door opened.
Maxie walked down the stairs to the street
to get her newspaper. She would try to hold
the door open with one foot as she reached
out to get the newspaper. But every morning
it was just a little too far for her to reach.
The door closed, and Maxie couldn't get back in.

So, at 8:20 every morning, Maxie had to ring
for Walter to let her in. Walter knew
it was Maxie. He would open the door
to let her in with her newspaper.

At 8:45 every morning, Maxie made a pot of tea.
All the people who lived in the brownstone heard
Maxie's tea kettle whistle. How Maxie loved
that whistle! She loved it so much that she let it
sing out for some time. Everyone heard the whistle.
And everyone knew that when the whistle stopped,
the time would be 8:46.

The mailman knew Maxie best of all. He knew
she had a sister who lived in another city.
He knew when Maxie planted the flowers
in her window boxes. Every spring
he would bring her the seeds in the mail.

Every morning at 9:00, Maxie walked
down the stairs to the street again
to see the mailman. By that time,
he was putting mail in the boxes of other people
who lived in the house. Maxie took her mail
and climbed back up the stairs. When she got
to her floor, she went into her apartment
and closed the door after her.

Who Needs Maxie?

One Monday afternoon at 1:05, just as she did every afternoon at 1:05, Maxie moved the bird into the living room. The cat moved to the back window and went back to sleep.

"You're very happy sleeping by the window day after day," Maxie said to the cat. "All you ever want to do is move from one window to another. You don't need anyone, and no one needs you. But you don't care."

Maxie walked away from the window. "I care," she said. Maxie went to bed.

That was Monday.

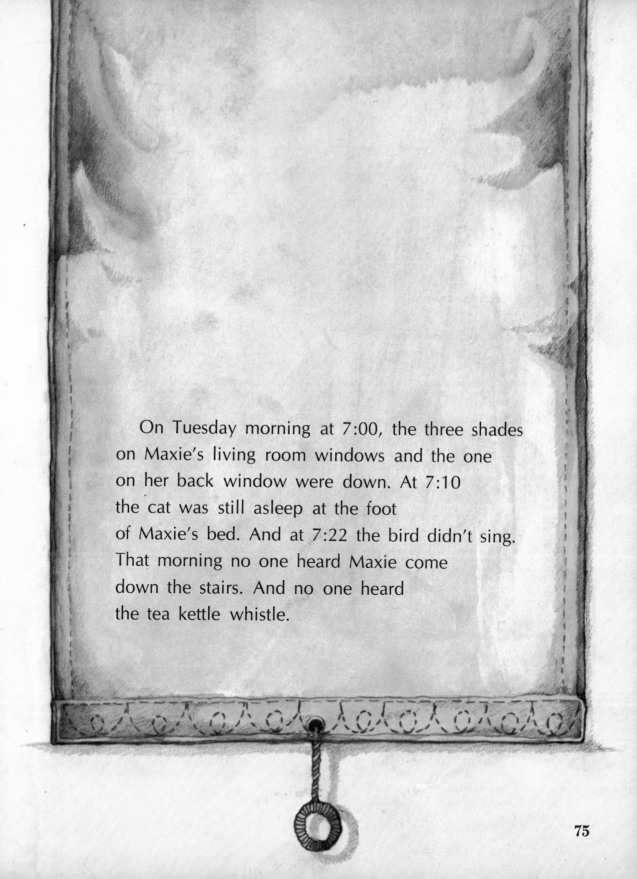

On Tuesday morning at 7:00, the three shades
on Maxie's living room windows and the one
on her back window were down. At 7:10
the cat was still asleep at the foot
of Maxie's bed. And at 7:22 the bird didn't sing.
That morning no one heard Maxie come
down the stairs. And no one heard
the tea kettle whistle.

At 9:00 the mailman came with the mail.
He had some seeds for Maxie, and he waited
for her to come down the stairs.
When she didn't come, he went up to her floor
to give them to her. He climbed the stairs
to Maxie's apartment and called her name.
He waited, but no one came to the door.

At 9:03 a man who lived in the brownstone
came up the stairs. At 9:05 Mrs. Greenhouse
came up. At 9:07 Mrs. Stone came over
from next door. Penny Parks came up at 9:10
with her brothers. Walter was the last one
to come up. By that time it was 9:17,
and all the people were waiting
for Maxie to open the door.

When Maxie didn't open the door,
Walter opened it, and all the people went in.
They found Maxie in bed. Someone called a doctor,
and he came right away. He went into Maxie's
bedroom and closed the door.

When the doctor came out, he said to the people,
"Maxie isn't sick. She's lonely.
She doesn't feel loved. She doesn't feel
that anyone needs her."

No one said anything.

Then Mrs. Stone walked into the bedroom.
"Maxie!" she said. "You and that bird let me down.
Every morning when the bird sings, I get Mr. Stone
out of bed. The bird didn't sing this morning,
and I didn't get up. Mr. Stone is still sleeping,
and now he won't be on time for work.
All because of you and that bird!"

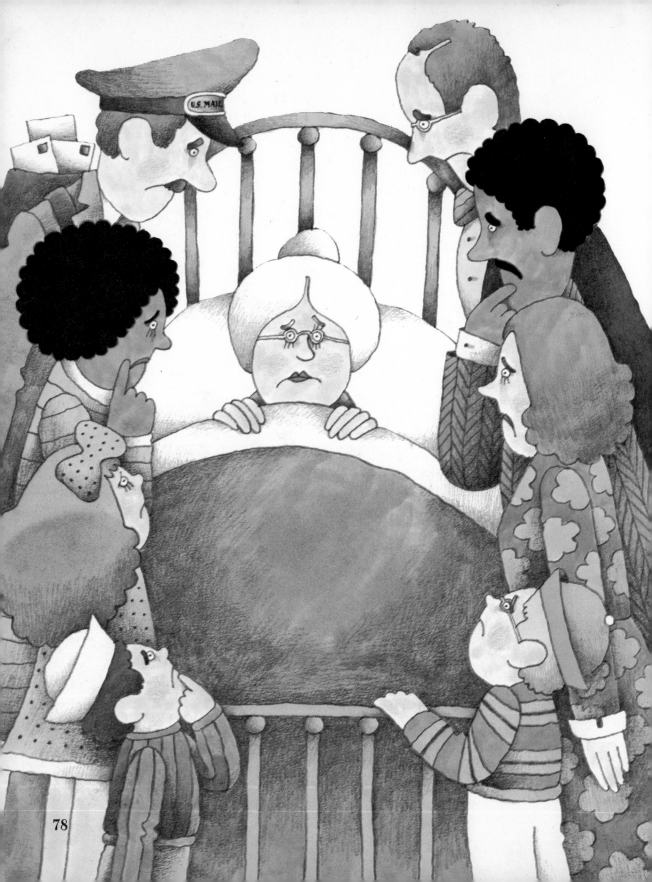

The other people went into the bedroom
and told Maxie how much they needed her.
Penny Parks didn't get up on time to go
to school because she hadn't heard the tea kettle
whistle. Mr. and Mrs. Greenhouse didn't get up
because they didn't see Maxie's shades go up.
And Walter didn't get up to paint an apartment
because Maxie didn't ring for him to let her in.

Maxie found out that everyone in the brownstone
needed her every morning. She was so happy,
she got out of bed and made a few pots of tea.
By 9:45 that morning, everyone had gone.
Maxie went over to the window boxes
and began to plant the new seeds
that had come in the mail.

Junk Day on Juniper Street

Lilian Moore

No one on Juniper Street can really say how it all began. Ben and Jenny say it began in their house. And Sandy says it really began in her backyard. But Mike says it began with his father.

One morning Mike's father was reading his newspaper. "Take a look at this!" he said to Mike's mother.

Do you have junk around your house? Then it's clean-up time!

"Do we have junk?" asked Mike.
"Hmmmm . . ." said his mother.

Then Mike's mother saw Sandy's mother
in the backyard. Mike's mother said,
"Look at this." And she showed her the newspaper.

"Do we have junk?" asked Sandy.
"*Hmmmm . . .*" said her mother.

Some mothers went to Ben and Jenny's house for tea. "Did you see this?" asked Sandy's mother. And she showed them the newspaper.

Jenny asked, "Do we have junk?"

All the mothers laughed. "We all have junk," they said. "Lots and lots of junk!"

Then someone said, "Let's do it! Let's have a Take-Out-All-the-Junk Day!"

So Juniper Street had a Junk Day.

It was clean-up time in every house.
Mothers and fathers and boys and girls walked
from one room to the next, saying, "Do we really
need this? Do we still want that?"

Then everyone began to put the old beds,
old clothes, old toys, and pictures and books
out on the street.

And every time people looked around the house,
they saw other things to take out—an old radio,
a white doghouse, a big old rocking chair.

In no time at all, there was junk by every house on Juniper Street. Mike's father looked up and down the street. "We're going to need a big truck to pick up all this junk!"

So Ben's father called up the junk man. "We have lots of junk on Juniper Street," he told the man. "You will need a big truck to take it all away."

"I have a big truck," said the junk man. "But I can't come today. I will come for your junk in the morning."

"Don't forget," said Ben's father, "a big truck."

All day people walked by the junk
on Juniper Street. No one could go by
WITHOUT looking at the junk.

Mike stopped at Sandy's house.
"Say," he said. "There's a good saw.
I need a saw like that to make my treehouse.
May I have it?"

Sandy's mother said yes.

Sandy's father stopped to look
at the junk by Mike's house.
He saw an old box.
"Why, it's just what I need!"
he said.

"Take it!" said Mike's father.

Jenny's mother saw a little table
she liked. "I need a little table
in my living room," she said.

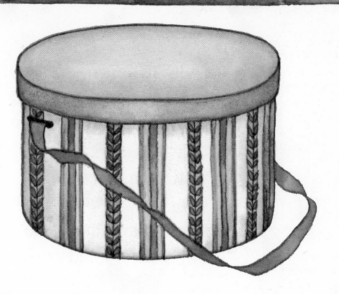

Sandy's mother found a big hatbox
in the junk by Jenny's house.
"I can put my big red hat in this,"
she said.

Jenny saw a doll bed in the junk
by one house. She put her doll
in the bed. "It's just right,"
she said.

So Jenny asked for the doll bed.

By this time everyone was looking
at the junk next door and the junk
up and down the street.

A man picked up a radio.
"Do you call this junk?" he said.
"I can have this radio working
in no time." And off he went with it.

An old lady took home a white
doghouse and put it in her backyard.
"Now I can get a dog," she said.

One man was happy to find a window box.
"I'll paint it green," he said,
"and put some red flowers in it."

An old man saw an old picture
of a river. "I lived by a river
when I was a boy," he said.
And he took the picture home.

By that night there was just one thing
on Juniper Street. It was a big rocking chair.
People stopped to look at it, but everyone said,
"Too big!"

So there it was.

The next morning a big truck came
down Juniper Street.

"Oh, my," said Ben's father. "We forgot
to tell the junk man not to come!"

The truck came on down the street and stopped.
A very big man got out of the truck.
He looked up and down the street.

All he saw was the rocking chair.
He walked over and looked at it. Then
he sat down and began to rock.

At last!
A big rocking chair!

Then he put the chair on his truck,
and off he went with all the junk
on Juniper Street.

Elizabeth Levy

The Giant Who Didn't Win

One summer day, in a place far away,
the townspeople were having an afternoon
of games. A giant who lived in a nearby castle
came by to play games, too. No one
really wanted a giant around, but no one knew
how to tell him not to come.

So the giant came, and he wanted to play
in all the games. The townspeople began
the afternoon with a game of bobbing for apples.
The giant tried, but he didn't win.
The one to win was someone from the town
of Stillwater.

The next game was to see who could paint
the best picture. The giant worked for a long time
on his picture, but he didn't win. Someone
from the town of Stillwater did. The giant said
to the man next to him, "You know, I really
thought I would win that one. I want to win
something this afternoon."

Then there was a game to see who could
sing the best. The giant made a lot of noise, but he
didn't win. Everyone said a lady from Stillwater
was the best. The giant said to anyone around,
"Who are these people from Stillwater?
I've never heard of them."

Soon the afternoon was over and the giant didn't win anything at all. The people from Stillwater were the ones to win everything.

That night the giant was sitting alone in his castle. He was feeling very mean. "I've got to find out where this town of Stillwater is," he said.

He went to his books and looked it up. "Here it is," he said. "Stillwater is near a big river. It doesn't look very far from here."

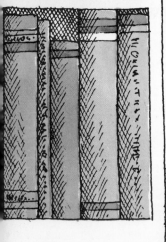

"I'm going to do something to the people
of Stillwater," said the giant. "I've got
to think of something really mean."

The giant walked from room to room,
trying to come up with an idea.

Then the giant laughed a mean laugh.
"I've got it!" he said. "I'll take a
big bag of dirt to Stillwater.
I'll dump the dirt into the river
that's near the town. The water
will come up and cover all the people and
all the town. What a good idea!"

The next day the giant got up, still feeling mean.
"I feel very mean today," he said. But no one was
around to hear him.

He put lots of dirt into a big bag, and he began
his trip to Stillwater. Only he forgot the book
that told him where Stillwater was, and he forgot
to bring along something to eat.

The giant walked all day and after some time,
he began to get hungry. The giant stopped a cobbler
who was coming along the road. The cobbler
was hungry, too, and he wanted to get home fast.
He had a big bag on his back, too, but his bag had
lots of old shoes in it.

The cobbler had just come from Stillwater.
The shoes were all owned by the townspeople.
He had picked up all the old shoes, and
he was taking them home to make them
look like new. Then he would take them back
to Stillwater, and everyone would pay him.

"Oh, Mr. Cobbler," said the giant. "Can you
tell me how far Stillwater is?"

The cobbler looked at the giant. The giant
was looking mean and hungry. "Why do you want
to go there?" asked the cobbler.

"I want to dump this bag of dirt
into their river," said the giant.
"The dirt will make the water
come up and cover the town.
I don't like the people in that town.
They didn't let me win anything
at their games one afternoon."

"Oh, oh," thought the cobbler.
"This will never do. If the giant
makes the water cover up Stillwater,
no one will be there to pay me
when I bring these shoes back."

The cobbler thought and thought. Then he said,
"You will never get to Stillwater today. Why, look
at me. I've just come from Stillwater. Look at
all these shoes I had to wear out just to get from there
to here." He showed the giant his bag of old shoes.

The giant sat down and cried.
"I'm hungry," he said,
"and I need my sleep.
I'll never make it
all the way to Stillwater.
I'm going back home
to my castle."

The giant dropped his bag of dirt where he had stopped.
This bag of dirt was as big as a hill. It was much
too big for anyone to move.

In time the people forgot all about the giant and his bag of dirt. But the hill is still there, and it is called Stonesthrow. No one knows why. You can go there if you want to. It's not very far from the town of Stillwater.

The Cobbler

Crooked heels
    And scuffy toes
Are all the kinds
    Of shoes he knows.

He patches up
    The broken places,
Sews the seams
    And shines their faces.

—Eleanor Alletta Chaffee

A Do-It-Yourself Storymaking Kit

One morning a _____ was going to the _____ when a _____ came by. The _____ didn't know what to do. He ran to the _____ to get the _____. The _____ was so surprised she got in a _____. She took a _____ and a _____ and a _____. No one ever saw the _____ again.

giant	backyard
lady	store
mailman	brownstone
child	farm
queen	castle

newspaper	bag
boat	chair
radio	doll
helicopter	rock
cow	table

Noun Marker. The words *a* and *the* signal the reader that a noun will follow. Have the children make up stories by filling in the missing nouns.

NO SWIMMING

George McCue

Jill, Ellen, Bob, and Edward were good friends.
They all lived near a beautiful little lake.
They thought they were very lucky to live
so near the water because they could go swimming
every day.

Sometimes Mr. Brown, who lived nearby,
went swimming with them.

One day the children went to Mr. Brown's house
to see if he wanted to go for a swim.
Mr. Brown said, "We can't go for a swim today.
Maybe we will never swim in the lake again."

"Why not?" asked Edward.

"Because the lake is polluted," said Mr. Brown. "There's a new sign at the lake. It was just put up today. It says:

"If we go into the water, we may get sick."

"What is making the lake polluted?" asked Jill.

"It could be a lot of things," said Mr. Brown. "Let's go down to the lake and look at it."

When Mr. Brown and the children got to the lake, they looked into the water. They saw that it wasn't clean. As they walked around the lake, they saw why.

"Look at that garbage floating in the water," said Jill. "That's what's polluting the water!"

As they walked on, Edward saw some oil on top of the water. "That oil is polluting the water, too," said Edward.

"Someone put tires in the lake," said Ellen. "Come over here and take a look!"

"Why would anyone throw tires into a lake?" asked Bob.

"Because they didn't stop to think,"
said Mr. Brown. "And the people who own
that factory over there are polluting
the water, too."

"Can we do anything about the pollution?"
Bob asked Mr. Brown.

"How can we make the water clean again?"
Ellen asked.

"There are some things we can do,"
said Mr. Brown. "I don't know if we can
ever make the lake really clean again,
but we can try."

"Maybe if people could see what they're doing
to the lake, they would stop polluting it,"
said Edward.

"I know what we can do," said Mr. Brown.
"I have a friend who takes pictures
for the newspaper. Let's go and talk to him.
Maybe we could get him to take some pictures
of the lake and put them in the newspaper.
Then everyone would know about the lake
being polluted. And then maybe everyone
would help clean up the lake."

The next day Mr. Brown and the children went to see Mr. Brown's friend at the newspaper. After they told him about the lake, they all went back to see it. Mr. Brown's friend took pictures of the garbage and the oil and the tires and the factory.

That night the pictures were in the newspaper. In a few days people all over town were talking about the pollution in their lake.

One morning lots of people in town went
down to the lake to clean out the garbage
and the tires.

The people who had boats on the lake began
to talk about ways to stop the oil from getting
into the water.

And people began to throw their garbage
into big cans that were set up around the lake.

And the people who owned the factory said
they would try to find ways to stop
polluting the water.

The people in the town knew it would take
a long time for the water to be clean again.
But they didn't give up. And one day
the sign came down. Jill, Ellen, Bob,
and Edward could go swimming again.

They had found out something about pollution.
Lots of things pollute the water.
Lots of people pollute it. We can have
beautiful clean water in our country,
but we all have to help.

Philip Ressner

Jerome

(A PLAY)

The Players

Jerome	Giant Bird
Witch	Dragon
Townspeople	Girl
Man	Wizard

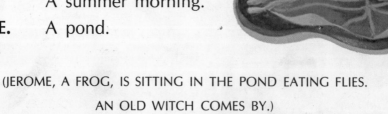

Act 1

TIME. A summer morning.

PLACE. A pond.

(JEROME, A FROG, IS SITTING IN THE POND EATING FLIES.
AN OLD WITCH COMES BY.)

Jerome. Hello, old witch.

Witch. I don't like being called a witch. I could turn you into a monster for saying that. But I think I'll turn you into a prince.

Jerome. I didn't mean to make you feel bad. I won't care if you turn me into a prince.

Witch. You may not like being a prince. We'll see. I'll walk around you three times. When I stop, you will be a prince.

(WITCH WALKS AROUND JEROME, SINGING.)

Witch. *A frog you are now,*
A prince you will be.
If you think I can't do it,
You just wait and see.

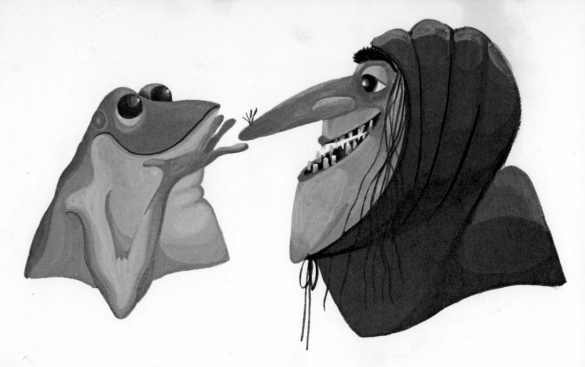

(WITCH STOPS WALKING.)

Jerome.   Did I turn into a prince?

Witch.   Yes, you did.

Jerome.   But I don't feel like a prince.

(WITCH LAUGHS.)

Witch.   Oh, you will. Now, you just go on into town and act like a prince.

Jerome.   I'll try. But I don't think it will work.

Witch.   Good luck!

Act 2

TIME.   The same morning.
PLACE.   A park in a small town.

(JEROME WALKS OVER TO SOME PEOPLE
SITTING ON A BENCH IN THE PARK.)

Jerome.   Hello. I'm the new prince who does
princely deeds.

(ALL THE TOWNSPEOPLE LAUGH.)

Man. So, you're a prince who does princely deeds! How would you like to do some for us?

Jerome. I'd be happy to help.

Man. Good. Now one thing we need is to get rid of the giant bird. He eats up all our corn.

Jerome. Just show me where the corn is. I'll see what I can do.

Man. Come with us. We'll take you there now. It's just the time of day for a princely deed.

(ALL THE TOWNSPEOPLE LAUGH AS THEY TAKE
JEROME TO SEE THE CORN.)

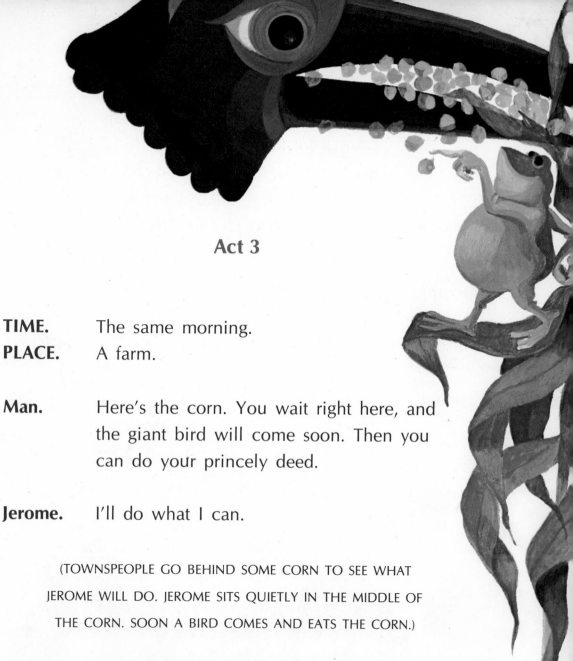

Act 3

TIME.	The same morning.
PLACE.	A farm.

Man. Here's the corn. You wait right here, and the giant bird will come soon. Then you can do your princely deed.

Jerome. I'll do what I can.

(TOWNSPEOPLE GO BEHIND SOME CORN TO SEE WHAT JEROME WILL DO. JEROME SITS QUIETLY IN THE MIDDLE OF THE CORN. SOON A BIRD COMES AND EATS THE CORN.)

Jerome. Stop! Stop eating the corn!

(BIRD LOOKS AT JEROME BUT GOES ON EATING THE CORN.)

Jerome. That isn't your corn. You can't eat it.

117

Bird. I have to. I'm a very big bird, and it takes a lot to fill me up. And if I don't eat all the corn, other animals could get some of it. How about you? Wouldn't you like to eat some of this corn?

Jerome. Not me. I eat only flies.

Bird. Really? You'd never eat any of this corn?

Jerome. Never. And I know some fish who would never eat corn. And some foxes, and some porcupines and raccoons! And I know that all tigers, camels, and bears would be happy never to eat corn.

Bird.   Thanks for telling me. As long as I'm the
only one eating the corn, I don't have to
eat it all right now.

(BIRD FLIES AWAY, SINGING, AS THE TOWNSPEOPLE COME

OUT FROM BEHIND THE CORN.)

Man.   You got rid of the bird!

Jerome.   Yes, he's gone. He will never eat all
your corn again, just some of it every now
and then.

Townspeople. Good work, Jerome. Our corn is saved!

Man. Now, how would you like to do another princely deed?

Jerome. I'd be happy to try.

Man. There's a dragon who burns our houses and forests. Will you help us get rid of him, too?

Jerome. Where is the dragon?

Man. He lives in a dark cave near a big hill. We'll take you there.

(EVERYONE WALKS OFF WITH JEROME.)

Act 4

TIME.   That afternoon.
PLACE.   A cave.

(JEROME IS LOOKING INTO THE CAVE. THE TOWNSPEOPLE
ARE BEHIND SOME BIG ROCKS.)

Jerome.   Dragon, come out here right now! I'm going
to get rid of you.

(DRAGON COMES OUT OF HIS CAVE.)

Dragon. Why?

Jerome. Because you've been burning people's houses and forests.

Dragon. I can't help it. You know what I mean?
I just can't help burning things.
I try not to, but I can't stop the fire.

Jerome. Then why not burn other things?

Dragon. What other things?

Jerome. How about burning garbage at the dump?

Dragon. H-m-m, garbage. Does the garbage smell bad?

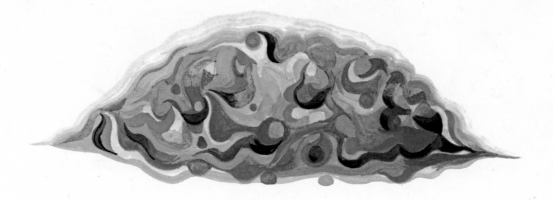

Jerome. Oh, yes. You would love the smell.

Dragon. Really? Does the garbage burn right away?

Jerome. Not right away. You have to work at it.
It's a little wet.

Dragon. Good. I like to work at things.

(JEROME AND THE DRAGON GO OFF TO THE DUMP. THE
TOWNSPEOPLE COME OUT FROM BEHIND THE ROCKS.)

Girl.   Maybe he really is a prince.

(TOWNSPEOPLE ALL LAUGH.)

Man.   He's just a frog. But maybe we could ask him to do one last princely deed.

(JEROME COMES BACK.)

Man.   Will you get rid of the bad wizard who lives in the dark forest and does mean things?

Jerome.   Just show me where he lives, and I'll see what I can do.

(JEROME AND THE TOWNSPEOPLE GO OFF
TO THE WIZARD'S HOUSE.)

Act 5

TIME.   That same day.

PLACE.   A stone house in the forest. It has no windows
and no door.

(THE TOWNSPEOPLE ARE BEHIND THE TREES. THE WIZARD IS SITTING ON
TOP OF THE HOUSE, LOOKING DOWN AT JEROME.)

Wizard.   Who are you?

Jerome.   I'm the prince who does princely deeds.

Wizard. You're a frog. I can smell a frog when I see one. What were you before you were a prince?

Jerome. A frog. What were you before you were a wizard?

Wizard. I guess I was a boy.

Jerome. Oh. Why did you stop being a boy?

Wizard. I thought it would be fun to be a wizard.

Jerome. That's too bad. Was it fun being a boy?

Wizard. Oh, was it ever! Climbing trees, fishing, playing in the mud, and running downhill so fast you couldn't stop! Oh, I wish I were a boy again!

(WIZARD JUMPS DOWN FROM HOUSE AND TURNS INTO A BOY.)

Boy. Oh, I forgot. Whatever I wish I get. I'm a boy again! I'm going to run downhill so fast I can't stop.

(BOY RUNS OFF. TOWNSPEOPLE COME OUT

FROM BEHIND THE TREES.)

Jerome. The wizard is gone. You won't see him ever again.

Townspeople. Jerome, you really are a prince!

(LITTLE GIRL GIVES HIM FLOWERS.)

Man. Before you go, we want you to have something for all your princely deeds. Do you see that little castle up on the hill? It's yours!

(JEROME LOOKS AT THE LITTLE CASTLE.)

Jerome. Thank you, but all I need is a pond.

Man. Not only does the castle have a pond, but there are lots of flies around it, too!

Jerome. Good. I'll move in right away. I haven't had a thing to eat all day!

(JEROME GOES OFF TO HIS CASTLE. THE TOWNSPEOPLE GO

BACK TO THE TOWN.)

Birthday Gift

I know that I could have a fish
A hamster or a rabbit.
A kitten or a puppy dog
Could be a pleasant habit.
The only pet I really want
Is just a smallish dragon
To follow me about the yard
And pull me in my wagon
And toast marshmallows with his nose
And snortle very gently
And give off little sparks at night
And curl up quite contently.

—Margaret Hillert

What's the Question?

Sentences that start with words like *who, what, where,* and *when* are almost always questions.

Who is that?
What day is it?
Where do you live?
When are we going home?

Finish these sentences. Will your sentences tell something or ask something?

Who ___ ___ ___?
What ___ ___ ___?
Where ___ ___ ___?
When ___ ___ ___?

Question Markers. Have the sentence at the top of the page and the questions below it read and discussed. Note the italicized words. Then let the children make up questions by filling in the blanks.

Four Scary Things

MARVIN'S

There's a big round thing on my street. I asked my mother,
"What's that?"

"It's a manhole cover, Marvin," she said.

"What's a manhole cover?" I asked.

"It's something that covers
up a manhole," she told me.

"But what's a manhole for?"

She told me that
there are pipes and things
under the street. If a man
has to work on them,
he goes down a special hole
to get to the pipes.
The hole he goes down
is a manhole.

MANHOLE

Winifred Rosen

But I didn't think that was right. I thought my mother
told me that because she didn't want me to go
down under the street to find out what
was really there. Maybe she thought
I'd fall into the manhole
if I took off the cover.

Maybe she thought I'd go down
into that hole and never
come back. Mothers are
like that. They think
you might never come
home from places.

But I had to know
what was really
under that manhole cover.

I thought there was a scary thing down there.
One day I went over to the manhole very quietly
so the scary thing wouldn't hear me. I waited
there for a long time. I didn't hear him
make any noise, but that didn't mean much.

I thought about that manhole every day. Some
days I would take my baseball bat and hit
the manhole cover and run away fast.
The scary thing never tried to get me.
But that didn't mean he wouldn't try.

What the scary thing liked was bread.
Sometimes before I went to bed, I put some
bread next to the manhole. I knew he liked it
because it was never there in the morning.

One time, when I was sitting near the manhole,
I heard a little noise. So I thought,
"The scary thing's got prisoners trapped
down there."

That night I put lots of bread near the manhole.
Only this time I said, "Give some of this
to your prisoners."

I didn't know if he would give the prisoners
any bread, so I thought I'd stay around.
Then if I heard his prisoners crying,
I'd hit him with my baseball bat
right in the middle of his manhole cover.
That would teach him!

One day I went over to the cover and called,
"Why don't you come out and play baseball."

The scary thing didn't say anything.
I didn't like that. So I hit that manhole cover
with my baseball bat again and again.
But it didn't do any good because the scary thing
still didn't come out. So I went home.

Then one morning I came downstairs,
and the manhole cover wasn't covering up
the manhole.

"The scary thing ran away," I thought.

So I looked under cars, in doorways,
behind garbage pails. I couldn't find
that scary thing.

Then I thought, "Maybe he went back
into his hole."

I looked into the manhole. Was it dark!
Then I saw a ladder going right down
into the manhole. I began to climb
down the ladder.

It got darker and darker.

Then I could feel something.

It wasn't the ladder.

It moved!

It was a man.

"What are you doing in a manhole?" he asked.
"There isn't anything down here but some pipes."

"Do you work on the pipes?" I asked.

"Yes," he said. "Now run along
and play baseball."

The next day I saw a funny-looking thing
on our street. It had bars and looked like a cage.

I asked my mother, "What's that cage for?"

She said, "That's no cage, Marvin.
That's just where the water goes down
under the street."

But I knew that wasn't right.

A cage is a cage.

Pretending

I have quite a handy habit.
When I hurry, I'm a rabbit.

When I'm buying chops and stew,
I'm a tiger—hungry, too!

When I meet a friendly horse,
I'm another horse, of course.

If you run and try to catch me,
I will vanish in the air.
And before you finish blinking,
I'm a most surprising bear.

So, if when you go out walking,
There's a fox behind a tree,
Don't be afraid and call for aid,
It's really only me.

—*Alice and Martin Provensen*

Elizabeth Levy

Something Queer at the Toy Store

Bobby looked around the toy store
and waited. He knew what he wanted
to get for his sister Linda,
and he didn't have much time.
But Mr. Konivi was with a policeman,
so Bobby just had to wait.

As Bobby waited he thought, "What's
a policeman doing in here?
Something queer is going on."

Bobby liked to think all the time about
what was really going on. And when he did,
he would tap his braces and say,
"Something queer is going on."

"Bobby," his mother would say,
"there isn't anything queer going on.
Now stop tapping your braces."

But Bobby's mother wasn't with him
in the toy store. So Bobby could tap
his braces and think about what was going on.
    The policeman was still there when
Mr. Konivi came over to Bobby.
Bobby thought he had heard
the policeman say something was missing.
Bobby wanted to know what it was,
but he didn't know how to find out.

"What can I do for you, Bobby?"
asked Mr. Konivi.

"It's my sister's birthday," said Bobby.
"I want to get her a necklace. I want the one
with the big green stone."

"I'll get it for you," said Mr. Konivi.
He reached for a necklace, but it was not
the one with the green stone.

"No, Mr. Konivi," said Bobby.
"Not the red necklace.
I want the green one."

"Oh, yes," said Mr. Konivi. He put away
the red one and picked up the green one.

Mr. Konivi put the necklace in a little box without saying anything to Bobby.

"Now why is he so quiet?" thought Bobby, tapping his braces. "I think he's upset about something. But what?"

Mr. Konivi went to talk to the policeman. But Bobby couldn't hear what they were saying. Bobby went home, but he knew something queer was going on at the toy store.

The next day was Linda's birthday.
There were games and singing and cookies.
Linda got lots of toys for her birthday,
but she told Bobby quietly that she liked
her necklace best.

After that, Bobby and Linda and their friends
played in the treehouse in the backyard.

From the treehouse Bobby could see
his mother coming out of the house
with the man who worked for Mr. Konivi.
Bobby began to tap his braces.

"Linda," said their mother. "Will you
come down? Bert is here from the toy store.
He says he has to take back the necklace
Bobby gave you."

"What!" said Linda, and everyone
in the treehouse looked down at Bert.

The Necklace Is Gone

Linda came down from the treehouse.
"Why do you want my necklace?"
she asked Bert.

"Mr. Konivi didn't know another boy
wanted that necklace," said Bert.
"He had come into the store before Bobby,
and I told him he could have it.
Mr. Konivi should never have let Bobby
take it. I came over with a more beautiful
necklace. If you'll give me the green one,
I'll give you this one. Then I can get back
to the store."

"I like my necklace," said Linda. "Why don't you give the other boy that one? After all, Bobby picked this one out for my birthday, and I want it."

"No. I can't do that," said Bert.

"I think you will just have to give it back, Linda," said their mother. "The one Bert has is very beautiful. Why don't you get yours and give it to Bert so you can go on playing."

"I'm not happy about it," said Linda. But she went back up into the treehouse to get the necklace.

"It's gone," called Linda from the treehouse.

"Gone!" cried Bert.

"It was on top of all the boxes,
and it's not here," said Linda.

"Look again," said their mother.
"Bobby, you help, too."

All the children helped, but no one could
find it.

"We can't find it, Mother," said Linda.
"It should be here, but it's not."

"Oh, no!" said Bert. "It's got to be there.
I'm going to take a look."

"Bert!" said Linda and Bobby's mother.
"You're too big to go up into the treehouse.
It's only for the children. I never go up there,
and their father never goes up.
Linda wouldn't hide the necklace.
If it were there, she would have told you."

"It's Linda's birthday. If we find the necklace,
we'll bring it to the store. After all,
it's only a toy. I think we should go now,"
she said. "The children want to play."

When Bobby's mother and Bert were gone,
everyone in the treehouse began to talk.

"Did someone hide it?"

"I didn't hide it; did you?"

"No. Bert really wanted it back, didn't he?"

"I don't like that man."

But Bobby didn't say anything. He just sat
tapping his braces. Then he said, "I have
the necklace." And he took it out
of his pocket.

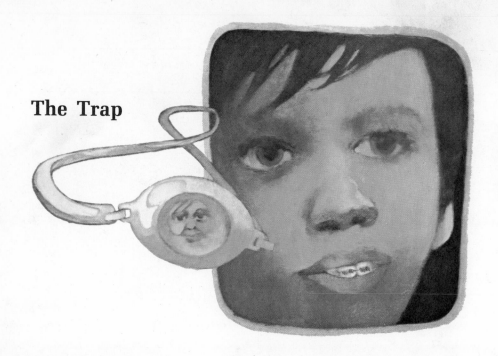

The Trap

Everyone looked at Bobby.

"Something queer is going on," said Bobby.
"Everything is not as it looks."

"What's the story, Bobby?"
one of the boys asked.

Bobby told them about the policeman
in the store and how Mr. Konivi tried
to give him the red necklace.

"I don't think another boy wants
this necklace," said Bobby. "I think Mr. Konivi
and Bert want it. And I don't think it's a toy.
I think Mr. Konivi has stolen things
in his toy store and this is a stolen necklace.
Mr. Konivi and Bert are crooks."

"You're right," said Linda. "They are crooks.
Let's go tell Mother."

So everyone climbed down from the treehouse
and ran to tell Bobby's mother about Bert
and Mr. Konivi. Bobby was tapping his braces
all the time, but this time
his mother didn't tell him to stop.

She said, "I think you're right, Bobby.
I'm going to call your father,
and then I'm going to call the police."

Bobby's father and the policeman came right away.
Bobby told his story again.

The policeman looked at Bobby and then
at Bobby's mother and father. "Bobby's right,"
he said. "We knew something was going on
at the toy store. But it's not Mr. Konivi;
it's Bert. I was just telling Mr. Konivi
to look out for Bert when Bobby came
into the store.

"Bert is part of a gang of crooks,"
the policeman went on to say. "We have been
after them for a long time, but until now
we just couldn't trap them. When Bert went
to work for Mr. Konivi, we thought
that the gang wanted to hide stolen things
in the toy store until they could sell them.
They thought no one would think of looking
for stolen things in a toy store.

"Bobby," said the policeman, "you would
make a very good policeman. You thought
this out all alone."

Bobby turned a little red. "But I thought
Mr. Konivi was a crook, too," he said.

"You were right about everything but that,"
said Bobby's father.

The policeman began to talk again. "I think
we can trap Bert. I know Bert and the gang
will try again to get the necklace back.
And I think they will try tonight when
it's dark and they think no one is here."

"I'll put the necklace back
in the treehouse," said Bobby.
"Then I'll hide there until the crooks
come to get it. Then I'll trap them."

"No, Bobby," said the policeman.
"That wouldn't be safe. But if you let me hide
in your treehouse, my men and I
will trap them with the necklace.
Then everyone will know they're a gang
of crooks."

"I want to see that," said Bobby.

"Me, too," said Linda.

"Me, too," said the other children.

"If we could, we would like to see it, too,"
said Linda and Bobby's mother and father.

"You'll have to stay in the house,
where it's safe," said the policeman.

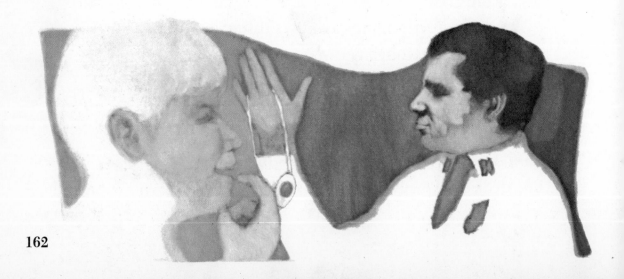

So that night everyone came to Bobby
and Linda's house. Mr. Konivi came, too.
He didn't like the gang thinking they could hide
stolen things in his toy store.

The policeman told everyone what to do.
"I want all of you to go into the house,
where it's safe. I don't want the gang
to see you. Put all the lights out
so they will think everyone is asleep.
I put the necklace in the treehouse.
I will hide in the tree, and my men will hide
in the backyard."
Everyone waited. It got very dark,
and no one could really see a thing.

And then, there by the flowers near the house,
something moved. Then someone ran over
to the tree and began to climb the rope.

No one moved after that. Everyone waited.
Everything was quiet.

Then they heard someone say, "What!"
and someone say, "Help!"

No one could see what was going on.
Then they saw the policeman coming
down the ladder with Bert.
The other police had the other men, too.
They put the crooks into their car
and took them away.

So the trap worked, and the police
got the gang at last. The story was
in the newspaper the next day.
Under the story was a picture
of Bobby and Linda and their friends
and Mr. Konivi, too. Bobby was the one
in the middle. But you knew that, didn't you?

Tammy Camps in the Rocky Mountains

Elizabeth Baker

Tammy sat up in her sleeping bag and looked at her father and her brother, Terry. "Why are you two up already?" she asked.

"Did you forget?" said Daddy.
"We're climbing Long's Peak today.
And we have to be down
before the noonday storm comes."

Tammy got up and got ready to go. Daddy put all the things they would need for the trip into the pack.

"Don't forget your camera, Tammy," said Terry. "You can get some good pictures at Long's Peak."

Tammy had taken pictures of just about everything
in the Rocky Mountains with her new camera.
She wanted to show her friend Ann
what it was like to go camping.

"Ann doesn't think camping is any fun,"
said Tammy. "But wait until she sees
my pictures."

Daddy, Terry, and Tammy went off up the trail.

"Stop, you two," Tammy said. "I want to take
a picture of you walking up the trail.
Daddy, get behind Terry so the pack will show."

When they got to a small stream running
down the mountain, Tammy made them stop
again. "Terry, you pick some mountain flowers,
and Daddy, you sit near the stream," she said.

Daddy and Terry laughed and did
as Tammy asked.

As they climbed to the part of the mountain
where there were no more trees,
Tammy stopped again.

"Daddy, get up on that big rock and look over
at the peak," said Tammy. Tammy walked
around and around him. At last she took
the picture.

"Now can we go?" Terry asked.

"Not yet," said Tammy. "Get up on the rock, and I'll take a picture of you."

"You have a picture of the Peak already," said Terry.

"But I want one from the other side," said Tammy. "I want Ann to see how far up the mountain we went."

"All right," Terry said. "But if we don't get going, we won't make it to Long's Peak before the storm."

"This is the last time, Tammy," Daddy said.
Tammy took the picture, and Daddy and Terry
went on up the trail. Tammy tried to stay
with them, but they were soon ahead of her.

Tammy heard a noise behind her. She turned
and saw some little animals looking at her
from behind some rocks. As quietly as she could,
she got out her camera. She was just about ready
to take their picture when Terry called,
"Tammy, come on up here."

The animals ran away, and Tammy walked up
to where her brother was waiting.

"Don't you know we don't have any time
for pictures?" Terry said.

Chasm Lake

Daddy looked at the sun. "I don't think
we can get all the way to the top before noon,"
he said. "What do you want to do?"

"Let's go on and see how far we can get,"
Terry said.

"That's not a good idea," said Daddy.
"What if we're up there when the storm comes?"

"I guess that wouldn't be so good," Terry said.
He turned to his sister. "You and your camera!"

173

"If we can't go to Long's Peak, let's go
to Chasm Lake," Tammy said. "Wouldn't that be
a good place to eat lunch?"

"I think it would," said Daddy, and he
and Terry and Tammy began walking again.
Along the way they saw a beautiful waterfall.

"I wish I could get a picture of it,"
said Tammy. "But I can't get one from here."

"There will be other things to take pictures of,"
Daddy said. He went on down the trail
with Tammy and Terry behind him.

"What's that little house?" Tammy asked.

"It's a place to stay if you're on the mountain in a storm," Daddy said.

"Can we go in it?" asked Tammy.

"In a few minutes," Daddy said. "Let's go and look at Chasm Lake first." Daddy began to climb the rocks behind the little house. Tammy and Terry went ahead of him. They wanted to see who could get to the top first.

"Oh, it's beautiful!" said Tammy as she looked over the side of a big rock and saw Chasm Lake for the first time. She got out her camera and took a picture.

"Come on down here," Terry called. "I'll take a picture of you with the lake behind you."

Tammy climbed down off the rock and walked over to the lake.

"I can't get you there," Terry said. "Back up."

Tammy started to back up, hit her foot on a rock, and sat down in the water.

"Oh, Terry, help! It's cold!" she cried. "Why didn't you tell me I was so near the water?"

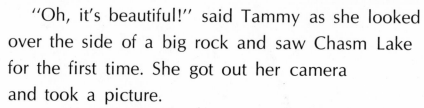

Terry helped her up and handed her the camera. "That should make a good picture," he laughed.

"Did you take one of me sitting in the water?" asked Tammy. "I'm never going to let you take a picture with my camera again."

"Let's go back to the little house," said Daddy. "Tammy can dry off there, and we can have lunch."

Tammy took a cover off the bed in the little house and put it around her. "It's cold in here," she said. "I'm going back out in the sun."

As they sat in the sun eating their lunch,
a big cloud came floating by. Soon the sky
began to get dark, and they couldn't see
the top of the mountain.

"Here comes the noonday storm,"
said Daddy. "Let's get back in the house."

Just as they got inside, the rain started.
They all looked out at the storm. It was
only a few minutes before the rain stopped
and the sun came out again.

"Time to go," said Daddy.

Tammy put the cover back on the bed,
and they started back along the trail.

Tammy's Last Picture

"Look at the waterfall now!" Tammy cried.
"There's a rainbow! I can get
a beautiful picture of that."

She ran up the trail until she got to a place
where she could take the picture.
She sat down on the side of the trail.
She slid down the mountain
a little until her feet rested on a big rock.
Then she took the picture.

"Tammy, come back here," Daddy called.

"Just one more picture," Tammy said.
"I want to get the rainbow again."

Tammy moved a little to get
another picture of the rainbow.
The rock her feet were resting on
started to move. It slid down the mountain,
and behind it slid Tammy, feet first.

"Daddy, help!" Tammy cried. She tried to stop
her fall by holding on to some small plants. But
the plants came up in her hands.
At last her feet found another rock,
and she came to a stop.

"Daddy, I'm afraid! What will I do?"
Tammy asked.

"Don't move, Tammy," Daddy said quietly.
"Don't look down."

"How will we get her up?" Terry asked.
"There's no telling how long that rock she's on
will stay in place."

"Get the rope from my pack," Daddy said.
Then he looked down at Tammy. "It's all right,
Tammy. We'll get you. Hold on. I'm going
to throw a rope down. We'll pull you up.
Here it comes, Tammy," said Daddy.

The rope fell down the mountain,
about a foot away from Tammy.

"I see it," Tammy called.
She got the rope and turned away
from the mountain.

"What are you doing?" Daddy cried.

"I'm going to take that picture," Tammy said.

"Look out, Tammy!" Daddy called.
"The rock is moving!"

Just as the rock slid down the mountain,
Tammy took the picture.
The big rock went faster and faster
down the mountain until they couldn't see it.
But Tammy was holding on to the rope.

183

"We'll get you up," Daddy said.
"Just hold on tight a few minutes more."

They started to pull Tammy up a little at a time.
Dirt and rocks slid out from under her and fell
down the mountain. But at last they got Tammy
back up on the trail.

Tammy ran to her Daddy and cried. "I was
so afraid," she said.

"It's all right, now, Tammy," Daddy said,
holding her tight. "It's all over,
and you don't have to be afraid now."

Tammy stopped crying. "My camera,"
she said. "Is my camera all right?"

Terry and Daddy looked at one another
and laughed. "Your camera is safe, Tammy,"
Daddy said. "Now let's go back down the trail."

Daddy, Terry, and Tammy started back
down the mountain. When Tammy stopped to take
a picture of a squirrel, Daddy took the camera
out of her hands.

"No more pictures on this trip, Tammy," he said.
"If Ann wants to know more about our trip
to the Rocky Mountains, you can tell her."

Follow Tammy's Trail

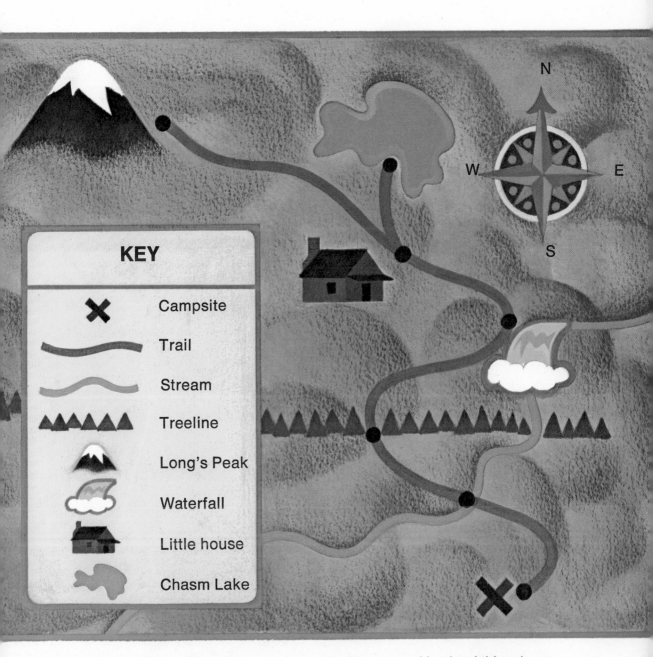

KEY

✖	Campsite
∿	Trail
∿	Stream
⋀⋀⋀	Treeline
🏔	Long's Peak
☁	Waterfall
🏠	Little house
🦴	Chasm Lake

Map Reading. Discuss the symbols used in the map, and let the children locate the places Tammy went. Discuss the directions north, south, east, and west.

Joan Lexau

The Potter and the Tiger

Once there was a potter who was looking
for his burro. It was a very dark night,
and it was raining.

"Come, my dear little burro," the potter called.
"Where are you, good little burro?"

To himself he said, "Wait till I get my hands
on that burro! It won't walk off anymore."

The potter couldn't see well because of the rain.
So he didn't know he was very near a tiger.
And when the tiger moved, the potter jumped
on it and gave it a hit and a kick.

"That's what you get for making me come out
on a night like this, burro," the potter said.
"Now come home."

No one had ever hit the tiger before.
He was so surprised, he let the potter
ride him home.

In the morning the potter's wife said,
"What did you ride home last night, my dear?"

"The burro," said the potter. "Why do you ask?"

"Look out there," said his wife.

The potter was very surprised to see the tiger.
"Oh dear, dear, dear," he said.
"That tiger could kill a man!
Did he do anything to me?"

His wife looked him over and told him
that he was all right.

Once the people saw the tiger
by the potter's house, the story got around.
From near and far, people came to hear
the potter tell the story himself.

The potter did not say that he had thought
the tiger was his burro. After telling
his story, he would say, "It was nothing,
really."

"Nothing! That big tiger has been around here
a long time. He made us afraid to go out
at night," a man said. "Now we're not afraid
anymore. The king should hear of this."

Some of the people went to the king and
told him about the potter's ride on the tiger.
The king was surprised to hear of a man
who could bring a tiger back to his house
with nothing but his two hands. Without waiting
to hear anymore, he told the people he wanted
to see this man for himself.

So the people took him to the potter's house
at once.

The potter gave the tiger to the king,
and the king gave the potter some land
and some houses.

When the king had gone, the potter said
to himself, "Well that's all over. I'll never ride
anything but a burro again."
But the potter didn't know
what was in store for him.

The Brave Little Potter

One day the king heard that an army
was coming to take over his castle.
The army was from another country.

The king called in his top men at once.
"Our army is too small. We cannot fight
such a big army," the men said to the king.
"We will have to give up."

"Not without a fight!" said the king.
"Is there no brave man who will lead
my army?"

"What about the potter?" asked one of the men.
"A man who could get a tiger with nothing
but his two hands could lead our army."

"Bring the potter to the castle," said the king.

The potter came to the castle and was surprised
to hear that he would lead the king's army.

"Who, me?" asked the potter.

"You, my brave man," said the king.

The brave potter was afraid to say no.
"Does the enemy have a big army?"
he asked the king.

"I don't know," said the king.

"I will go out alone to see how big
their army is," said the potter.

The potter went home. "Wife," he said.
"I have to ride out to look at the enemy army.
The burro has not come back, so go and
find me a horse. I have never been on a horse,
so get me a little one. I mean a pony.
I mean a little pony."

He waited for her to say he must not go.
He was a potter and not a man to lead
an army. But she went out and got a little pony
for him to ride.

The potter looked at it. "Couldn't you find
a smaller one than that?" he asked.

"There is no smaller pony than this one,"
said his wife.

Just then a man came from the king. With him
was a charger.

"The king wants you to ride this horse,"
the man said.

"Oh dear, dear, dear," said the potter.
"Well, I can't ride the pony when the king wants
me to ride this horse." He waited for his wife
to say he could ride the pony after all.

"This charger will go much faster
than that little pony," she said.

"I know, I know," said the potter. He looked
at the charger and said he would not go just yet.
He would go at night. "After all, I want to see
the enemy, but I don't want them to see me,"
he said.

The Potter Rides Again

As soon as it was dark, the potter's wife
told him it was time to go.

"Not yet, not yet," the potter said. "Let it get
a little darker."

"It won't get any darker than this,"
said his wife. And she went to get the horse.

The potter got on the horse. But he found
that he was looking one way and the horse
was looking the other.

"This is no good," said the potter. "I must see where I'm going." He jumped off and got on the right way.

"Quick," he said to his wife. "Put a rope around me so I won't fall off this horse."

His wife did as she was told. He waited for her to say he must not go. He waited for her to say if the horse did not kill him, the enemy would.

"Well," said the potter.

"Take care," said the wife.

The charger began to kick and jump, and then the potter was off.

"Didn't you hear
my wife say to take care?"
the potter said to the horse.

The charger ran so fast, the potter
couldn't see where they were going.
The charger ran all night, and in the morning
they came to the enemy camp. The potter
wanted to go around the camp.
He did not want to charge through it
so the enemy could kill him.

"Stop! Stop!" he said to the charger.
But the horse would not stop.

"Oh dear, dear, dear, what will I do?"
asked the potter. He saw a little tree
and took hold of it to stop the horse.
But the charger was going so fast that the tree
came up in the potter's hands.

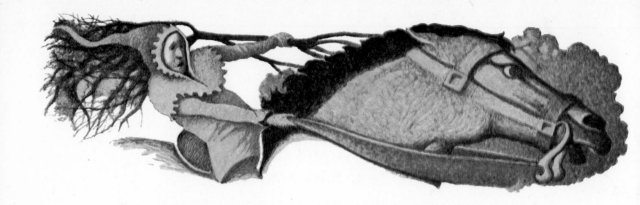

Some of the men in the enemy camp saw him.
"Look! Look at that man
on that big charger. He is so mad
that he is picking up trees as he rides,"
said one man.

"The rest of his army must be coming
behind him. If they are all like him,
we'll be killed," another man said.

They ran to tell their king that a big army
was coming and picking up trees as they came.

"We can't fight men like that!" they said.
"Quick! Quick! Let's get out of here.
We'll be killed if we stay and fight!"

The king and his men got away as fast
as they could. Only one man stayed behind.
He was too afraid to move.

The potter didn't fall off the horse
until he got to the enemy camp. He waited
for the enemy to kill him. The horse stopped.
It could not run anymore. The potter waited
and waited. At last he looked around and saw
the man who had stayed behind. The man told
the potter that his army had run away.
There would be no fight. He asked the potter
if he was going to kill him.

"No," said the potter. "I'm not going
to kill anyone. You may go home."

The potter couldn't wait to get back
to his house, where it was safe.
He was through riding horses, so he took
the charger and walked home.
When he got home, it was dark. His wife saw
him through the window and ran out
of the house.

"I was so afraid you would be killed,"
she said. "I didn't want you to go."

"**Now** you tell me," the potter said.

He called a man over and told him to go
to the king. "Tell the king I will be
at the castle in the morning. And thank him
for letting me ride that beautiful horse."

In the morning the potter set out on foot
to see the king. A man who saw him
along the way said, "All by himself,
he made the enemy run away. Yet he comes
to the king on foot."

"Yes," said another man. "He could come
on a beautiful horse as any other man would.
But he doesn't want to show how brave a man
he really is."

The king came out of the castle and thanked the potter for his brave deed. "You may have anything you want," said the king. "Just ask, and it will be yours."

"There is only one thing I want,"
said the potter. "Never to ride a horse again!"

Limerick

There was a young lady of Niger
Who smiled as she rode on a tiger;
They returned from the ride
With the lady inside,
And the smile on the face of the tiger.
—Cosmo Monkhouse

How Would You Feel?

The Treehouse

Dina Anastasio

On the morning of her birthday, Lisa climbed
the big apple tree in her backyard. She knew
she shouldn't be climbing a tree in her new clothes.
But Lisa didn't care. She wanted to be safely
in her treehouse when the children started
coming to her party.

Every time Lisa thought about the party,
she got a funny feeling inside.
"It's going to be just horrible," she thought.

First of all, the party was her mother's
idea—not Lisa's. And besides that, Lisa and
her family were new in town. Lisa didn't
really know the children who were coming
to her party. She had met them the first day
at her new school. And she wanted to be friends
with them. But Lisa was shy with new people.

Lisa's mother thought that a party would be
a good way for Lisa to get to know the other
children. But as Lisa sat in her treehouse, she
was feeling so shy she just wanted to hide.
That's why she thought the birthday party
was going to be horrible.

Before long Lisa heard a car coming down the
street. It stopped at her house and three girls
got out. Lisa could hear her mother and father
talking to the girls. Lisa's father called her, but
Lisa didn't answer. Soon more children came
to the party. Lisa's father called again. But
still she didn't answer.

So Lisa's father went over to the apple tree
and picked up the telephone he and Lisa
had made. He tapped on it three times.
Lisa picked up her telephone.

"Hello," said Lisa.

"Is this Miss Lisa Stone?" asked her father.

"Yes," said Lisa.

"Miss Stone," said her father, "your name
has been picked from a bowl filled with names.
You, lucky lady that you are, will win a beautiful
brown kitten IF you can answer just one small
question. Are you ready, Miss Stone?"

"Yes, I'm ready," Lisa laughed.

"All right, Miss Stone," said her father.
"Here is the question. What is white
on the outside and green on the inside?"

Lisa laughed and laughed, and then
her father began to laugh, too.

"Your time is up, Miss Stone," he said.
"It's too bad you couldn't answer the question."

"Wait, wait," she cried. "The answer is —
a frog sandwich!"

"Right," her father said, laughing. "A frog
sandwich! You win. A very shy kitten
and a very happy birthday are waiting for you,
if you're ready to come down now."

Lisa put down the telephone and climbed
down the big tree.

"A frog sandwich—really!" her father laughed
as Lisa ran to him. When she reached him, he
handed her the little brown and white kitten.

Lisa walked shyly over to the children
to show them her kitten.

After that Lisa's birthday wasn't horrible at all.
It was one of the best she had ever had.
By the time the party was over,
Lisa had ten new friends—and a kitten!

My Love for You

I love you little, I love you lots;
My love for you would fill two pots,
Fifteen buckets, sixteen cans,
Three teacups and four dishpans.

—Unknown

One Word – Two Meanings

I saw the <u>crane</u> fly away.
The <u>crane</u> picked up a load of dirt.

I like to <u>watch</u> TV.
My <u>watch</u> says five o'clock.

Pull up the <u>shade.</u>
We sat in the <u>shade.</u>

I ran so fast, I had to <u>rest.</u>
You can have the <u>rest</u> of the cookies.

Multiple Meanings. Have the sentences read and the meanings of the under-
lined words discussed in each pair. Let the children choose the picture that fits
each sentence.

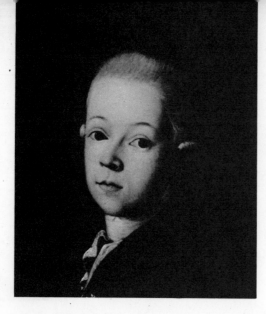

THE MUSIC OF MOZART

Elizabeth Levy

One day, a long time ago, the Mozart family
set out on a trip to see the king and queen.

The king and queen loved good music.
And because they were the king and queen,
they could hear the best music in the world.
Whenever they heard about someone
who played music very well,
they asked him to come to the castle.

And that is why the Mozarts were
on their way to the castle. The Mozart children
were going to play for the king and queen.

Wolfgang and Nannerl Mozart were very special.
They were still children. But they could
play music as well as people
who had been playing for years and years.

Nannerl was older than Wolfgang,
and she could play very well.
But Wolfgang could play like
no other child who had ever lived.
He started playing music when he was
only three years old. And when he was five,
he wrote such beautiful music
that people still like to hear it today.

MUSÉE CONDÉ, CHANTILLY

The day that the Mozart family went
to the castle, Wolfgang and Nannerl put on
their best clothes. Their mother and father
wanted them to look right and to act right
at the castle.

But when Wolfgang saw the king and queen,
he did something that surprised everyone.
He ran up to the queen and gave her a kiss.
The queen was very surprised, but she liked it.
She laughed at Wolfgang.
Then she asked everyone to sit down.

Nannerl played first, then Wolfgang.
Then the two children played together.
Their music was so beautiful, the queen began
to cry a little. The king and queen loved
the music so much, they asked the Mozarts
to come back to the castle again and again.

One time when Wolfgang was playing
for the king, the king said, "Your playing is
very beautiful with two hands. But what can
you play with one hand?"

So Wolfgang put one hand behind his back.
He showed the king how well he could play
with one hand.

Then the king said, "You play well
when you see what you are doing.
But what can you do
with your eyes covered?"

So Wolfgang's eyes were covered,
and still he played beautiful music.

When Wolfgang was alone with his father,
he told him that he didn't like doing tricks
for the king. Wolfgang said that he loved music
too much to play tricks with it.

When Wolfgang and Nannerl were at the castle,
they did not have to play music all day.
The king and queen had children of their own.
Some of them were about as old as Wolfgang
and Nannerl. The king's children and Wolfgang
and Nannerl played together all over the castle.

One day as Wolfgang was running with two
of the king's little girls, he fell.
One of the girls, Marie Antoinette, stopped
to help him up. Her sister went on walking.
Wolfgang thanked Marie Antoinette
for helping him. "When I grow up,
I will marry you," he said to her.

Marie Antoinette did not marry Wolfgang.
She was to become a queen. But
she never forgot the times
she and Wolfgang played together
when they were children.

Wolfgang wrote more and more music
as the years went by. Here is a part
of some music that Wolfgang wrote
when he was still only five years old.

Try to find someone to play it for you. Isn't it happy music? Can you see why the beautiful music Wolfgang Mozart wrote years and years ago is still played today?

Read the Ending!

safe + ly = safely
brave + ly = bravely
shy + ly = shyly
quick + ly = quickly

Always play *safely.*
Firemen work *bravely.*
Mary sang *shyly.*
Ted ran *quickly.*

Which word means *in a shy way?*
Which word means *in a quick way?*
Which word means *in a brave way?*
Which word means *in a safe way?*

What other words end with *ly?*

Suffix *ly.* Point out the base words plus endings at the top of the page. Have them read in sentences. Then let the children answer the questions.

Boy, Was I Mad!

Kathryn Hitte

I was mad one day.
I mean I was really mad.
So I ran away.

I put some cookies
in my pocket
and ran out
of my house fast.

And I didn't look back.

I wouldn't look back at that house
for anything. I was so mad that day—
that day I ran away.

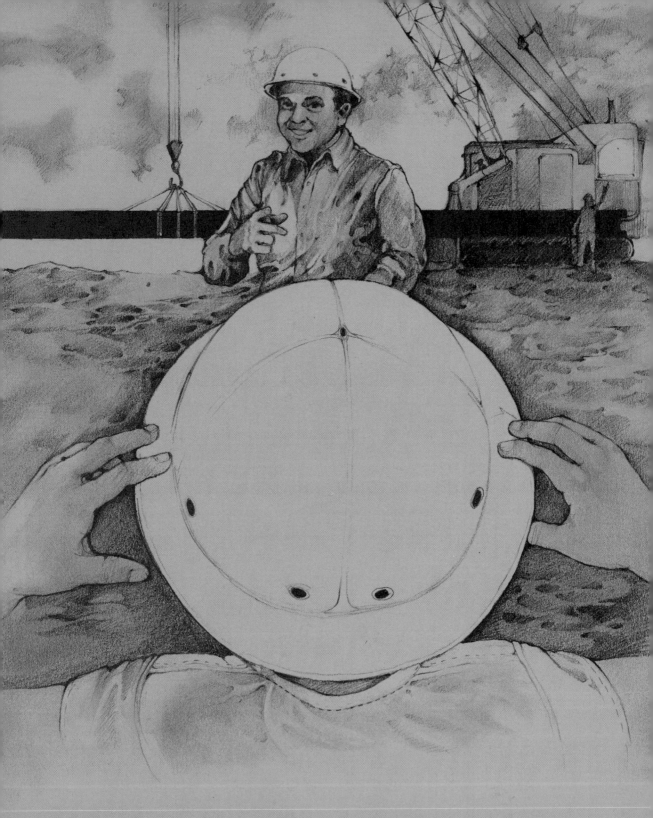

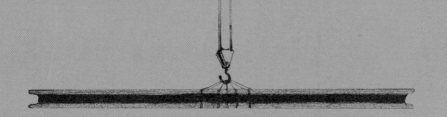

I turned the corner, and there was a crane
out over the street. Men were climbing
and working and yelling. And that crane
went up and up.

I'd like to work a thing like that crane.
I think someday I will.

"Boy!" I said. "Look at that!"

One of the workmen laughed and gave me
a hat to wear. Just like his!

It was great at that place. It was so great
I just about forgot how mad I was. But
then I remembered and went on my way.

Around the next corner I met a junk
wagon. I knew that horse and wagon. The
junk man gave me a ride—he does that a lot.

"I might have a horse of my own someday,"
I said. "I think someday I will."

It was fun on that wagon. Then I
remembered how mad I was, so I climbed
down.

I saw a dog that was after a cat, and I watched them go. Then I stopped to pet another dog, and three more old dogs came running up to me. They all began to run after me up the street. It was fun, but then I remembered I was mad.

"Look, dogs," I said. "I can't play with you now. I'm running away, see? So let me alone. Go on, go back where you came from! Go home!"

But they still walked along with me. There isn't a dog that doesn't like me. I might have lots of dogs of my own someday. I think someday I will.

Well, then I saw a lot of ants in a place
in the sidewalk. Ants are about the best
thing there is to watch.

If I hadn't been so mad, I could have stayed
there and watched the ants all day.

Around the next corner I saw Tim
and his dad and his grandma.

"We're going to the park," Tim said.
"Come along with us, Ted!" (That's me.)

I like to run and talk and horse around
in the park with Tim. I was mad, but—

"All right," I said. "I'll go."

We got to the park, and Tim's dad and
grandma sat down on a bench to talk. But
Tim and I did tricks and things like
walking on our hands.

And we climbed around on some big rocks
and watched the clouds. And we thought
about how it is that birds know how to fly.
We had a great day.

When I came home, there was a moon in
the sky. That was funny because it was still
daylight. I never saw the moon in the
daytime before.

"I bet I go to the moon someday," I said.
"I'm going to get to that old moon.
You wait and see!"

Then just as I got to my house I thought.
"I FORGOT! I'm HOME! I was going to run
away. What should I do?"

Well it was time to eat, and something
smelled good. Boy, did I eat! And it was a
funny thing, but I just wasn't mad anymore.

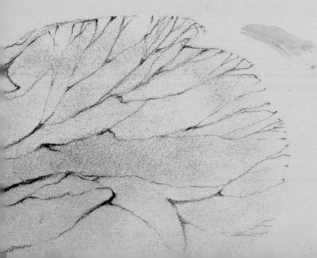

When I told my mother about how I forgot
I was running away, she said, "Oh, Teddy,
I'm so happy you forgot and came back
home."

"Me, too," I said.

My mother didn't have to tell me to get
ready for bed. Boy, did it feel good, that bed.

That was some day—that day when
I ran away.

Angry

Sometimes when the day is bad
And someone's made me very mad
Or I've been given angry stares,
I go behind the front porch stairs.

There, curled up with chin on knee,
I like to be alone with me
And listen to the people talk
And hurry by me on the walk.

There I sit without a sound,
And draw stick pictures on the ground.
If I should tire of it all,
I throw some pebbles at the wall.

After I've been there awhile
And find that I can almost smile,
I brush me off and count to ten
And try to start the day again.

—Marci Ridlon

William Wiesner

Happy-Go-Lucky

One afternoon a farmer was walking along the road from town. His clothes were covered with mud and dirt.

"Whatever happened to you?" asked his neighbor.

"I went to town to sell my cow," said the farmer.

"How much did you get for her?" asked the neighbor.

"Nothing," said the farmer as he sat down in his neighbor's rocking chair.

"Oh, my," cried the neighbor. "Your wife will be very mad at you."

"Oh, no," said the farmer. "My wife is very good. She won't say anything to me."

"Oh, really?" laughed the neighbor. "When she hears what you did, she'll run you out of the house. Not for twenty gold crowns would I want to be in your place."

"H-m-m," said the farmer. "I'll bet you twenty crowns that my wife will not be mad at me."

"All right," said the neighbor. "It's a bet!"

"Come home with me and stay behind the door," said the farmer. "You will see."

The neighbor did as he was told and hid
behind the door when the farmer went
into his house.

"Hello, my dear," said the farmer.

"Hello, my love," said the wife, and she put
the kettle over the fire. "How was your day?"

"Not good, not bad, dear wife," said the farmer.
"When I took the cow to town, it started to rain,
and soon I was covered with mud. When I got
to town at last, I found out
that the other farmers had gone home.
So I couldn't sell the cow," he said.

"I turned back right away but was soon very wet.
Just when I thought I couldn't walk
anymore, a man came by leading a burro.
Right away I thought how wonderful
it would be to come home riding a burro.
So I gave the man the cow,
and he gave me his burro."

"How wonderful!" said the wife. "Just think
how the neighbors will look at us as we ride
around town on our burro. Where is the burro?
I want to see it."

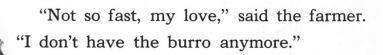

"Not so fast, my love," said the farmer.
"I don't have the burro anymore."

"What happened to it?" asked the wife.

"Just as I got on the burro's back, it started
to jump and kick all over the place. I tried
to hold on as best I could, but that burro was
too much for me. I fell off into the mud,"
said the farmer.

"Just then a man came by, leading a pig.
When he saw me in such a sad state, he said
he would give me his pig for my burro.
I thought that was a good idea.
So he went away on the burro,
and I walked on with the pig."

"Wonderful!" cried the farmer's wife.
"It's better to walk than to ride. And besides,
with a pig, our neighbors will know
that we eat well."

"Wait a minute, my dear," said the farmer.
"We don't have a pig anymore."

"What happened to it?" asked the wife.

"As soon as its owner was gone, the pig lay down
in the mud in the middle of the road
and wouldn't move," the farmer told his wife.
"I tried everything to get that pig
out of the mud. I tried to pull it. I kicked it.
I gave it some bread. But the pig just lay
in the mud and wouldn't move. Just as I was
about to give up, a man came by with a goat.
He told me that it was better to have a goat
than a pig because I would get along much faster.

So I gave him the pig, and he gave me the goat."

"You really think of everything!" said the wife.
"A pig eats so much and it needs so much care;
and when you're all through,
all you can do is eat it.
But a goat—that's a good animal to own.
It eats very little, and it doesn't need much care."

"Just a minute, my dear. We have no goat,"
said the farmer.

"What happened to it?" asked the wife.

"As soon as I took the rope, the goat started
to run very fast," said the farmer. "We ran
and ran until I hit a tree. Then we stopped.
As I picked myself up, a man came along
holding a rooster. When he saw me,
he stopped and told me that the goat
was too much for me. Life would be
better for me if I took his rooster. So I did."

"Oh, you wonderful man!" cried the wife.
"Now I won't have to take care of a goat.
It's good to have a rooster because it's better
than any clock. It will get us up on time
in the morning."

"You're right, my dear," said the farmer.
"The rooster would be better than a clock,
but I don't have the rooster anymore."

"What happened to it?" asked the wife.

"As I was walking along with the rooster,
I began to feel sick. I thought I would
never reach home. Not far away I saw a sign
that said, 'Doctor.' I went in and sold
the rooster for a pill to make me well
again. The pill worked. As I walked home,
I began to feel better."

"You were right to go to the doctor,"
said the wife. "Who needs a rooster?
We will get up whenever we want in the morning.
The only thing I care about is
that you are well again."

Without turning around, the farmer put
one hand through the open door.
The neighbor gave him
the twenty gold crowns,
then closed the door quietly.

"My good wife," said the farmer. "I'm happy
to be home, and I did bring you something
after all. Just before I got home this afternoon,
I made a bet with my neighbor
for twenty gold crowns. Luck was with me,
and I got the twenty crowns. And here it is!"

"You really are a wonderful man," said the wife.

The farmer and his wife sat down by the fire
to have their fish and tea. They were very happy.

the sun

I told the Sun that I was glad,
　　I'm sure I don't know why;
Somehow the pleasant way he had
　　Of shining in the sky,
Just put a notion in my head
　　That wouldn't it be fun
If, walking on the hill, I said
　　"I'm happy" to the Sun.

—John Drinkwater

252

New Words

The words listed beside the page numbers below are introduced in *People Need People*, Level 9 in THE HOLT BASIC READING SYSTEM. Italicized words can be identified from previously taught skills.

12. boat
stone
13. *wasn't*
croak
hands
14. *away*
pocket
15. *saying*
Mays
16. *fishing*
bait
anyone's
17. Miss
Penny
I'd
18. *picking*
19. pond
20. *onto*
22. Lucy
Lucy's
clean
coming
today
23. mud
monsters
24. *mother's*
getting
fat
25. *elevators*
26. *times*
radio
quietly
oh
you're
27. *asleep*

crying
28. under
covers
having
29. *become*
still
33. special ·
name
Indian
hunter
34. *walks*
making
bright
feathers
feather
36. *rabbit's*
foot
lucky
38. snapping
porcupine
quills
porcupines
puts
few
quill
picker
39. around
porcupine's
40. river
finding
bobbing
42. pants
covered
trying
44. *wet*

Albert
clouds
cloud
floating
along
rained
rain
schoolwork
45. top
Albert's
family
let's
idea
46. *set*
whenever
anyone
sun
cows
whatever
life
48. drought
summer
dried
rivers
49. *how*
wouldn't
50. farmers
farms
51. harvest
fall
took
world
helicopter
bringing
52. nothing

drop
ever
you'll
somewhere
54. Rumpelstiltskin
daughter
king
spin
gold
straw
55. castle
cry
funny-looking
56. give
man's
58. *ring*
queen
59. child
60. *became*
61. guess
names
62. *Appleflower*
Greenpot
Crabtree
63. *Birdwing*
Whitecoat
Tigerbutton
64. *queen's*
thanked
65. *Goodfish*
Pennypond
cried
70. Maxie
brownstone
shades

Maxie's
living
windows
shade
knew
71. stairs
newspaper
hold
closed
72. tea
kettle
whistle
73. mailman
planted
mail
74. needs
Monday
moved
move
need
75. Tuesday
76. *Greenhouse*
Parks
77. *she's*
doesn't
feel
sings
79. *needed*
hadn't
pots
80. junk
Juniper
really
backyard
81. *Sandy's*
showed
82. *mothers*
Jenny's
83. *fathers*
rocking
chair

84. *we're*
Ben's
86. table
87. *hatbox*
doll
88. *call*
working
91. *rock*
92. giant
win
townspeople
nearby
Stillwater
93. these
never
94. *feeling*
mean
95. bag
dirt
dump
cover
96. hungry
cobbler
shoes
97. *owned*
taking
pay
99. *hill*
100. *Stonesthrow*
104. *swimming*
lake
children
Brown's
105. polluted
106. garbage
what's
polluting
oil
tires
107. think
factory

pollution
108. *they're*
talk
109. *talking*
110. *boats*
ways
cans
111. *pollute*
112. Jerome
players
witch
dragon
wizard
act
flies
113. turn
prince
we'll
114. *stops*
laughs
luck
115. *does*
princely
deeds
116. rid
eats
corn
deed
117. farm
here's
soon
behind
118. *fill*
you'd
foxes
raccoons
tigers
camels
120. *saved*
burns
forests

121. *rocks*
122. you've
burning
people's
burn
124. *wizard's*
126. *before*
127. *climbing*
running
downhill
fast
turns
128. *runs*
gives
129. *yours*
haven't
134. *Marvin's*
round
Marvin
pipes
135. *manhole*
might
136. scary
hear
baseball
bat
hit
bread
137. *thing's*
prisoners
trapped
stay
139. *downstairs*
covering
doorways
pails
ladder
darker
143. *bars*
cage
146. *queer*

254

daytime

bet

242. farmer

happened

neighbor

neighbor's

243. hears

she'll

twenty

crowns

244. hid

245. leading

wonderful

burro's

246. sad

farmer's

better

neighbors

minute

247. owner

lay

kicked

goat

248. myself

rooster

249. sold

pill

250. turning